6-10

Printed at the Mathematical Centre at Amsterdam, 49, 2nd Boerhaavestraat, The Netherlands.

The Mathematical Centre, founded the 11th of February 1946, is a non-profit institution aiming at the promotion of pure mathematics and its applications, and is sponsored by the Netherlands Government through the Netherlands Organization for the Advancement of Pure Research (Z.W.O.) and the Central Organization for Applied Scientific Research in the Netherlands (T.N.O.), by the Municipality of Amsterdam and by several industries.

MATHEMATICAL CENTRE TRACTS

21

MATHEMATICAL CENTRE TRACTS

21

THE COMPACTNESS OPERATOR IN SET THEORY AND TOPOLOGY

BY

E. WATTEL

MATHEMATISCH CENTRUM AMSTERDAM

1968

CONTENTS

INTRODUCTION iii

CHAPTER I A GENERALIZATION OF ALEXANDER'S THEOREM 1

1. Alexander's subbase theorem 2
2. The compactness operator 6
3. A strengthening of Alexander's theorem 14

CHAPTER II ANTISPACES 25

1. C-spaces 26
2. Minusspaces and antispaces 32
3. Subspaces and sumspaces of antispaces 38

CHAPTER III CHARACTERIZATION OF THE NOTION OF COMPACTNESS 50

1. Characterization of compact spaces and the compactness operator 51
2. Collections of compact subsets and problems 55

REFERENCES 59

SUBJECT INDEX 61

INTRODUCTION

This tract is based on the papers [4], [5], [6], [11] and [12]. Together with De Groot, Strecker and Herrlich I studied the background and some generalizations of the isomorphism principle of [4]. The results of these investigations have been or will soon be published in [5], [6], [11], [12] and in this tract. In general we will not refer to these papers.

Several problems related to the isomorphism principle were solved by investigating the notion of compactness from a set-theoretical point of view. Alexander's subbase theorem was crucial in this context and therefore we give a detailed proof and a set-theoretical reformation of this well known theorem in the first section of the first chapter.

The second section of this chapter contains the definition of the compactness operator ρ which assigns to every collection $\mathfrak{S}$ of subsets of a given set X the collection $\rho\mathfrak{S}$ of all subsets of X which are compact relative to $\mathfrak{S}$. (In the sequel compactness relative to a system $\mathfrak{S}$ will always mean compactness relative to $\mathfrak{S}$ if $\mathfrak{S}$ is considered as a closed subbase.) We also introduce an auxiliary operator γ which can be called the "topology generating" operator. We prove that ρ and γ generate a finite semigroup under the usual compositions. For a more detailed study of this semigroup we refer to [6].

In the third section of the first chapter we obtain the most important results of this chapter, namely, a strengthening of Alexander's subbase theorem. To be explicit, let X be a set, let $\mathfrak{S}$ be a collection of subsets of X and let $\tilde{\mathfrak{S}} = \rho(\mathfrak{S} \cup \rho^2\mathfrak{S})$, then $\rho\tilde{\mathfrak{S}} = \rho\mathfrak{S}$ and moreover, in many important cases (e.g. if $\mathfrak{S}$ is a closed subbase for a Hausdorff space on X), $\tilde{\mathfrak{S}}$ is the unique maximal collection of subsets of X with the property that $\rho\mathfrak{S} = \rho\tilde{\mathfrak{S}}$. The results of this section are also published in [11].

In the second chapter we investigate a topological isomorphism principle. Following [4] we introduce the notion of a minusspace, which is an ordered pair $(X,\mathfrak{G})$ consisting of a set X and a collection of subsets $\mathfrak{G}$ which satisfies the equality $\gamma\mathfrak{G} = \mathfrak{G}$. We also introduce the notion of an antispace which is a minusspace $(X,\mathfrak{G})$ with the property that $\rho^2\mathfrak{G} = \mathfrak{G}$. The most important class of antispaces is the class of topological antispaces or C-spaces. This class is closely related to the class of compactly generated spaces and contains, for example, all metric spaces and all locally compact Hausdorff spaces. In the first section we give a survey of the theory of C-spaces. The results published in this section are slight generalizations of well known results for compactly generated spaces. However, the last proposition of this section contains an essentially stronger result and is important for the characterization of the compactness operator in the class of C-spaces.

The second section of this chapter contains, in addition to the basic definitions, an application of the third section of chapter I which provides some correspondences between the class of all spaces in which compact implies closed and the class of all compact antispaces. We were able to describe the k-expansions (compare with [1]) in this context.

The main results of the third section of the second chapter are published here for the first time. In this section we introduce the notion of an antisubspace. We will consider a characterization of the class of all antispaces and of the class of all isomorphic images of C-spaces, i.e. the class of C^*-spaces, which is based on the notion of an antisubspace. Although the class of C-spaces is not closed under the forming of subspaces, it follows that the class of all antispaces and the class of all C^*-spaces are both closed under the forming of antisubspaces.

In the third chapter we consider the following problem: Give necessary and sufficient conditions for a collection $\mathfrak{C}$ of subsets of a given set X which guarantee that $\mathfrak{C}$ is the collection of all compact subsets relative to some family of subsets of X. This problem appeared to be difficult and we only give partial solutions to it. We also give in this chapter a characterization of the compactness operator ρ in the class of Tychonoff spaces and in the class of C-spaces. We conclude this tract with some problems which are related to the characterization of the notion of compactness and which may be used for further investigations of this subject.

I want to express my gratitude to Prof.Dr. J. de Groot and to Dr. G.E. Strecker for their stimulating discussions and remarks.

I am grateful to Prof.Dr. M.A. Maurice and to Dr. G.A. Jensen who kindly read the manuscript.

I am indebted to Mrs. H. Roqué, to Mr. D. Zwarst and Mr. J. Suiker for the typing and printing of this tract.

Chapter I

A generalization of Alexander's theorem

Alexander's subbase theorem (cf. [7], p. 139) states that a set is compact if and only if it is compact with respect to a closed (or open) subbase of the topology. (Because of our needs in the following we shall prefer to talk about closed subbases). Since every collection of subsets generates (as a closed subbase) a topology, we can assign to every collection $\mathfrak{S}$ of subsets of a fixed set X the collection $\rho\mathfrak{S}$ of subsets of X which consists of all subsets of X which are compact relative to $\mathfrak{S}$. Thus we define an operator ρ which assigns to every collection of subsets of some set the family of compact sets relative to that collection of sets. This operator is called the compactness operator.

In the first section, in an introduction to the topic, we give some basic definitions and a detailed proof of Alexander's theorem and its set-theoretical reformulation which we need in this tract. In the second section we study the compactness operator and its basic properties. The third section is primarily concerned with deriving a strengthening of Alexander's theorem.

1. Alexander's subbase theorem

1.1. Definition. Let $(X,\mathfrak{T})$ be a topological space. A collection $\mathfrak{B}$ of subsets of X is called a closed base for $\mathfrak{T}$ if and only if every set is closed iff it is the intersection of members of $\mathfrak{B}$.

A collection $\mathfrak{S}$ of subsets of X is called a closed subbase for $\mathfrak{T}$ iff the family of all finite unions of members of $\mathfrak{S}$ is a closed base for $\mathfrak{T}$.

1.2. Remark. Any family $\mathfrak{S}$ of subsets of X may serve as a subbase for a (uniquely determined) topology $\mathfrak{T}$. (Observe that $\mathfrak{S}$ may be empty).

This is true because of the fact that in the definition, intersections and unions of empty families are permitted. (For example, if $\mathfrak{S} = \emptyset$, then $\mathfrak{T} = \{\emptyset, X\}$).

However, for later purposes (see in particular theorem 2.5 and the remark in 2.4) we would like to avoid this latter convention (see also definition 2.2).

To be explicit, we make the following agreement: If $\mathfrak{S}$ is any family of subsets of X, then by an intersection (a union) of members of $\mathfrak{S}$ we shall always mean an intersection (a union) of a non-empty subfamily of $\mathfrak{S}$. If $\mathfrak{S} = \emptyset$, then the family of all intersections and the family of all unions is also empty.

With this convention it is no longer true that any family $\mathfrak{S}$ of subsets of X is a closed subbase for a topology. Since the only sets which might be excluded from the topology are the sets $\emptyset$ and X, we agree that the topology $\mathfrak{T}$ generated by $\mathfrak{S}$ will be the topology generated by the subbase $\mathfrak{S} \cup \{\emptyset\} \cup \{X\}$ (taking only unions and intersections of non-empty families).

1.3. Definition. A system $\mathfrak{S}'$ of subsets of a set X is called centered iff every finite intersection of members of $\mathfrak{S}'$ is non-empty. A system $\mathfrak{S}'$ of subsets is called centered in A or A-centered, provided that $\mathfrak{S}' \cup \{A\}$ is centered, i.e., the collection $\{S \cap A \mid S \in \mathfrak{S}'\}$ is centered.

1.4. Definition. Let X be a set and $\mathfrak{S}$ a collection of subsets of X. A set $A \subset X$ is called $\mathfrak{S}$-compact or compact relative to $\mathfrak{S}$ provided that every A-centered subsystem $\mathfrak{S}'$ of $\mathfrak{S}$ has a non-empty intersection with A.

$$\text{i.e. } (\bigcap \mathfrak{S}') \cap A \neq \emptyset .$$

Observe that $A \subset X$ is also $\mathfrak{S}$-compact if no member of $\mathfrak{S}$ has a non-empty intersection with A. (In particular $A = \emptyset$ is $\mathfrak{S}$-compact).

1.5. Lemma. Let X be a set and let $\mathfrak{S}$ be an arbitrary system of subsets of X. If $\mathfrak{S}'$ is a centered subsystem of $\mathfrak{S}$, then there exists a maximal centered subfamily $\tilde{\mathfrak{S}}$ of $\mathfrak{S}$ which contains $\mathfrak{S}'$.

Proof. The proof of this lemma is a straightforward application of Zorn's lemma.

1.6. Lemma (Key lemma).
Let $\tilde{\mathfrak{S}}$ be a maximal centered subfamily of a system of sets $\mathfrak{S}$ and assume that $\tilde{\mathfrak{S}}$ contains a set $S = \bigcup_{i=1}^{n} S_i$ such that every S_i is a member of $\mathfrak{S}$. Then at least one of the S_i belongs to $\tilde{\mathfrak{S}}$.

Proof. Suppose that no S_i belongs to $\tilde{\mathfrak{S}}$. Then for every i, the system $\tilde{\mathfrak{S}} \cup \{S_i\}$ is not centered and there must exist a finite subfamily $\{S_{ik}\}$ of $\tilde{\mathfrak{S}}$ such that

$$(\bigcap_k S_{ik}) \cap S_i = \emptyset.$$

Therefore

$$(\bigcap_{i=1}^{n} (\bigcap_k S_{ik})) \cap (\bigcup_{i=1}^{n} S_i) = \emptyset,$$

and

$$(\bigcap_{i=1}^{n} (\bigcap_k S_{ik})) \cap S = \emptyset.$$

However, this is a contradiction, since $\tilde{\tilde{\mathfrak{S}}}$ is centered. We conclude that at least one of the S_i must belong to $\tilde{\mathfrak{S}}$.

<u>1.7. Proposition</u>. If a set X is compact relative to a family $\mathfrak{S}$ of subsets of X, then it is also compact relative to the family $\mathfrak{S}^\vee$ consisting of all finite unions of members of $\mathfrak{S}$.

Proof. Suppose that $\mathfrak{S}'$ is a centered subsystem of $\mathfrak{S}^\vee$. Then $\mathfrak{S}'$ is contained in a maximal centered subsystem $\tilde{\tilde{\mathfrak{S}}}$ of $\mathfrak{S}^\vee$ (cf. 1.5). Since every member of $\tilde{\mathfrak{S}}$ can be written as a finite union of members of $\mathfrak{S}$ (which are also members of $\mathfrak{S}^\vee$), lemma 1.6 implies that every member of $\tilde{\tilde{\mathfrak{S}}}$ has a subset which belongs to $\tilde{\tilde{\mathfrak{S}}} \cap \mathfrak{S}$. It follows that $\bigcap \tilde{\tilde{\mathfrak{S}}} \doteq$ $= \bigcap (\tilde{\tilde{\mathfrak{S}}} \cap \mathfrak{S})$.
Moreover, $\mathfrak{S}' \subset \tilde{\tilde{\mathfrak{S}}}$ implies that

$$\bigcap \tilde{\tilde{\mathfrak{S}}} \subset \bigcap \mathfrak{S}'.$$

The system $\tilde{\tilde{\mathfrak{S}}} \cap \mathfrak{S}$ is centered and, consequently, $\bigcap\mathfrak{S}' \neq \emptyset$ follows from the fact that X is $\mathfrak{S}$-compact. This proves that X is compact relative to $\mathfrak{S}^\vee$.

<u>1.8. Proposition</u>. If a set X is compact relative to a family $\mathfrak{S}$ of subsets of X, then X is also compact relative to the family $\mathfrak{S}^\cap$ consisting of all intersections of members of $\mathfrak{S}$.

Proof. Let $\mathfrak{S}'$ be a centered subfamily of $\mathfrak{S}^\cap$. Then every member of $\mathfrak{S}'$ is the intersection of a collection of members of $\mathfrak{S}$. We define

$$\mathfrak{S}'' = \{S \mid S \in \mathfrak{S} \;\&\; (\exists\, S' \in \mathfrak{S}')(S' \subset S)\}.$$

$\mathfrak{S}''$ is centered because $\mathfrak{S}'$ is centered.
Moreover, $\mathfrak{S}'' \subset \mathfrak{S}$ and X is $\mathfrak{S}$-compact. Consequently $\bigcap \mathfrak{S}'' \neq \emptyset$, and hence $\bigcap \mathfrak{S}' \neq \emptyset$. This implies that X is compact relative to $\mathfrak{S}^\cap$.

<u>1.9. Alexander's subbase theorem</u>.
A (non-empty) set X is compact relative to a family $\mathfrak{S}$ of subsets of X iff X is compact relative to the family $\mathfrak{G}$ consisting of all intersections of finite unions of members of $\mathfrak{S}$, i.e., $\mathfrak{G} = (\mathfrak{S}^\vee)^\cap$.

Proof. The sufficiency is clear. The necessity follows immediately from propositions 1.7 and 1.8.

Topological reformulation. A topological space $(X,\mathfrak{T})$ is compact if and only if it is compact relative to an arbitrary closed subbase for the topology $\mathfrak{T}$.

1.10. Remark. By relativization one can prove that a subset A of a set X is compact relative to a family $\mathfrak{S}$ of subsets of X iff A is compact relative to the family $\mathfrak{G}$ consisting of all intersections of finite unions of members of $\mathfrak{S}$. We reformulate this result as follows.

1.11. Theorem. The family of compact sets relative to a collection of subsets $\mathfrak{S}$ of a set X is equal to the family of compact sets relative to the collection consisting of all intersections of finite unions of members of $\mathfrak{S}$.

This theorem is fundamental throughout this tract.

2. The compactness operator

In this section the compactness operator ρ is defined and its basic properties are studied. As an aid in the investigation of ρ we define another operator γ which can be called the "topology generating" operator. It will be shown that with the usual compositions ρ and γ generate a finite semigroup. Its structure will be determined.

2.1. Definition. Let X be a (non-empty) set and let $\mathfrak{S}$ be a collection of subsets of X.We denote by $\rho_X\mathfrak{S}$ the family of all $\mathfrak{S}$-compact subsets of X. ρ_X willbe considered as an operator defined on the family of all collections of subsets of X. We call ρ_X the compactness operator on X. If confusion seems unlikely, we shall write $\rho\mathfrak{S}$ instead of $\rho_X\mathfrak{S}$.

We make two observations.

1) $\rho_X\mathfrak{S}$ is never empty ($\rho_X\emptyset = \mathfrak{P}(X)$) [1].

2) If $\mathfrak{S} \subset \mathfrak{T}$ then $\rho\mathfrak{T} \subset \rho\mathfrak{S}$.

2.2. Definition. Let X be a set. If $\mathfrak{S}$ is a collection of subsets of X, then we denote by $\gamma_X\mathfrak{S}$ the collection of all intersections of finite unions of members of $\mathfrak{S}$.

According to our agreement in remark 1.2, in this definition unions and intersections of empty families are not allowed. (Note that $\gamma_X\emptyset = \emptyset$.)

2.3. Remark. Observe that both γ_X and ρ_X are mappings from the set $\mathfrak{P}(\mathfrak{P}(X))$ [1] into itself. Therefore we may consider compositions between those operators which are defined in the usual way as compositions of mappings.

In particular we obtain powers of operators. If we let $\rho_X^1 = \rho_X$, then we define for every natural number n

$$\rho_X^{n+1}(\mathfrak{S}) = \rho_X(\rho_X^n(\mathfrak{S}))$$

for every collection $\mathfrak{S}$ of subsets of X. The collection $\rho_X^2\mathfrak{S}$ is called

---

1) The power-set of a set X will be denoted by $\mathfrak{P}(X)$.

the collection of <u>$\mathfrak{S}$-squarecompact</u> subsets of X.

Observe that $\gamma_X \mathfrak{S}$ is independent of X in the following sense: If Y is any set such that $\bigcup\mathfrak{S} \subset Y$, then $\gamma_Y \mathfrak{S} = \gamma_X \mathfrak{S}$.

We will usually omit the index X in the notation of both single and composite operators.

From these definitions it is immediate that

$$(1)\quad \gamma \circ \gamma = \gamma$$
$$\text{i.e. } \gamma(\gamma\mathfrak{S}) = \gamma\mathfrak{S} \text{ for every } \mathfrak{S}\,.$$

Furthermore, theorem 1.11, which is itself a reformulation of Alexander's theorem, can be formulated as

$$(2)\quad \rho \circ \gamma = \rho$$
$$\text{i.e. } \rho(\gamma\mathfrak{S}) = \rho\mathfrak{S} \text{ for every } \mathfrak{S}\,.$$

<u>2.4. Lemma</u>. Let X be a set and let $\mathfrak{S}$ be a collection of subsets of X. Assume that C is an $\mathfrak{S}$-compact set and E is $\mathfrak{S}$-squarecompact. Then $C \cap E$ is both $\mathfrak{S}$-compact and $\mathfrak{S}$-squarecompact.

$$\text{i.e. } (C \in \rho\mathfrak{S} \;\&\; E \in \rho^2\mathfrak{S}) \Rightarrow (C \cap E \in \rho\mathfrak{S} \cap \rho^2\mathfrak{S})\,.$$

Proof. (i) Suppose that $\mathfrak{C}'$ is a subsystem of $\rho\mathfrak{S}$ which is centered in $C \cap E$. Then $\mathfrak{C}' \cup \{C\}$ is a subsystem of $\rho\mathfrak{S}$ which is centered in E, and so the fact that E is $\mathfrak{S}$-squarecompact implies that

$$(\bigcap (\mathfrak{C}' \cup \{C\})) \cap E \neq \emptyset.$$

This intersection is equal to

$$(\bigcap \mathfrak{C}') \cap (C \cap E)$$

and therefore $C \cap E$ is squarecompact.

(ii) Let $\mathfrak{S}'$ be a subsystem of $\mathfrak{S}$ which is centered in $C \cap E$. Then the system

$$\mathfrak{S}'' = \{S \cap C \mid S \in \mathfrak{S}'\}$$

is a subsystem of $\rho\mathfrak{S}$, since every member of $\mathfrak{S}''$ is the intersection of a set of $\mathfrak{S}$ and a set which is compact relative to $\mathfrak{S}$. Furthermore, the system $\mathfrak{S}''$ is centered in E and thus

$$(\bigcap \mathfrak{S}'') \cap E \neq \emptyset,$$

$$(\bigcap \mathfrak{S}') \cap (C \cap E) \neq \emptyset,$$

which implies that $C \cap E$ is compact relative to $\mathfrak{S}$. The two parts together prove the lemma.

It is well known that finite unions of compact sets are compact and in certain (but not all!) topological spaces (e.g. Hausdorff spaces) also the intersection of a (non-empty!) collection of compact sets is compact. The next theorem shows that in any space finite unions and arbitrary intersections of squarecompact subsets are again squarecompact.

<u>2.5. Theorem</u>. Let X be a set and let $\mathfrak{S}$ be a collection of subsets of X. Then a finite union of members of $\rho^2\mathfrak{S}$ is a member of $\rho^2\mathfrak{S}$ and every intersection of a (non-empty!) subfamily of $\rho^2\mathfrak{S}$ is a member of $\rho^2\mathfrak{S}$.

The content of the preceding theorem can also be formulated as

$$(3) \quad \gamma \circ \rho^2 = \rho^2$$

i.e. $\gamma(\rho^2\mathfrak{S}) = \rho^2\mathfrak{S}$ for every $\mathfrak{S}$.

Proof. $\rho^2\mathfrak{S}$ is the collection of compact sets relative to $\rho\mathfrak{S}$ and therefore a finite union of members of $\rho^2\mathfrak{S}$ is a member of $\rho^2\mathfrak{S}$.

To prove the second assertion, let $\mathfrak{E}'$ be a non-empty subfamily of $\rho^2\mathfrak{S}$, and let $E_0 = \bigcap \mathfrak{E}'$. We will show that E_0 belongs to $\rho^2\mathfrak{S}$. Note first that if E_0 is empty, then it is squarecompact since there can be no subsystem of $\rho\mathfrak{S}$ which is centered in E_0. Thus we may assume that E_0 is not empty. Let $\mathfrak{C}'$ be a subsystem of $\rho\mathfrak{S}$ which is centered in E_0. In order to prove that

$$(\bigcap \mathfrak{C}') \cap E_0 \neq \emptyset,$$

we introduce another centered system, namely,

$$\mathfrak{C}'' = \{C \cap E \mid C \in \mathfrak{C}' \ \&\ E \in \mathfrak{E}'\}.$$

Every member of $\mathfrak{C}''$ is $\mathfrak{S}$-compact by lemma 2.4. Let E_1 be a member of

$\mathfrak{C}'$, then $\mathfrak{C}''$ is centered in E_1. From the fact that E_1 is $\mathfrak{S}$-square-compact it follows that

$$(\cap \mathfrak{C}'') \cap E_1 \neq \emptyset.$$

We conclude that

$$\emptyset \neq (\cap \mathfrak{C}'') \cap E_1 = \cap \mathfrak{C}'' = (\cap \mathfrak{C}') \cap E_0.$$

This proves our theorem.

2.6. Proposition. Let X be a set and let $\mathfrak{S}$ be a collection of subsets of X. Then $\rho\mathfrak{S} \subset \rho^3\mathfrak{S}$.

Proof. Let $C \in \rho\mathfrak{S}$ and let $\mathfrak{C}'$ be a (non-void) subcollection of $\rho^2\mathfrak{S}$ which is centered in C. By lemma 2.4 the system

$$\mathfrak{C}'' = \{C \cap E | E \in \mathfrak{C}'\}$$

is a subsystem of $\rho\mathfrak{S}$. Moreover, if E_1 is an arbitrary member of $\mathfrak{C}'$ ($\subset \rho^2\mathfrak{S}$) then $\mathfrak{C}''$ is centered in E_1 and so

$$(\cap \mathfrak{C}'') \cap E_1 \neq \emptyset.$$

It follows that

$$(\cap \mathfrak{C}') \cap C = \cap \mathfrak{C}'' = (\cap \mathfrak{C}'') \cap E_1 \neq \emptyset.$$

Consequently $C \in \rho^3\mathfrak{S}$ and hence

$$\rho\mathfrak{S} \subset \rho^3\mathfrak{S}.$$

2.7. Theorem. If X is a set and $\mathfrak{S}$ is a collection of subsets of X, then

$$\rho^2\mathfrak{S} = \rho^4\mathfrak{S}.$$

Proof. Proposition 2.6 applied to $\rho\mathfrak{S}$ yields

$$\rho^2\mathfrak{S} \subset \rho^4\mathfrak{S}.$$

To prove the opposite inclusion, we suppose that E is a member of $\rho^4\mathfrak{S}$ and $\mathfrak{C}'$ is a subsystem of $\rho\mathfrak{S}$ which is centered in E. Then by proposition 2.6, $\mathfrak{C}' \subset \rho^3\mathfrak{S}$ and therefore

$$(\cap\, \mathfrak{C}') \cap E \neq \emptyset.$$

This implies that $E \in \rho^2\mathfrak{S}$ and $\rho^4\mathfrak{S} \subset \rho^2\mathfrak{S}$.
We conclude that $\rho^4\mathfrak{S} = \rho^2\mathfrak{S}$.

We may restate the preceding theorem as follows

$$(4)\ \rho^4 = \rho^2.$$

2.8. Remark. In this section we have found four relations between ρ and γ

$$(1)\ \gamma \circ \gamma = \gamma,$$

$$(2)\ \rho \circ \gamma = \rho,$$

$$(3)\ \gamma \circ \rho^2 = \rho^2,$$

$$(4)\ \rho^4 = \rho^2.$$

It is now easily verified that ρ and γ generate a semigroup with the following multiplication table.

$\mathfrak{S}$	γ	ρ	ρ^2	ρ^3	$\gamma\rho$
γ	γ	$\gamma\rho$	ρ^2	ρ^3	$\gamma\rho$
ρ	ρ	ρ^2	ρ^3	ρ^2	ρ^2
ρ^2	ρ^2	ρ^3	ρ^2	ρ^3	ρ^3
ρ^3	ρ^3	ρ^2	ρ^3	ρ^2	ρ^2
$\gamma\rho$	$\gamma\rho$	ρ^2	ρ^3	ρ^2	ρ^2

In this table γ is a right unity, and ρ^2 is an idempotent. Associativity follows from the definition.

We now exhibit an example of a set X together with a collection $\mathfrak{S}$ of subsets such that all elements of the corresponding semigroup are distinct. It is clear that in this example $\mathfrak{S}$ cannot generate a Hausdorff topology, since in that case we always have $\gamma\rho = \rho$.

Example. Let X be the cartesian product of the set of all ordinals less than the first uncountable one and a two point set. We will denote

the points of X by (α,s). Let $\mathfrak{S}$ be the collection of subsets of X which consists of all singletons and of all sets S which are the inverse image, under the canonical projection, of closed subsets of the ordinals in the order-topology. This collection $\mathfrak{S}$ is not closed under finite unions and hence $\gamma\mathfrak{S}$ is not equal to $\mathfrak{S}$. The collection $\rho\mathfrak{S}$ consists of all subsets of X whose image, under the canonical mapping into the set of ordinals with the order-topology, is compact. The collection $\gamma\rho\mathfrak{S}$ consists of precisely all of the countable subsets of X, and the collection $\rho^2\mathfrak{S}$ consists of all finite subsets of X and hence every subset of X is a member of $\rho^3\mathfrak{S}$.
It follows that all collections are distinct.

This example shows that in general there do not exist other defining relations between ρ and γ in the semigroup than the four which are mentioned above.

We conclude this section with some further results concerning the operator ρ and its powers.
Note that the next two propositions are closely related to 2.4.

2.9. Proposition. Let X be a set and let $\mathfrak{S}$ be a collection of subsets of X. If n is any natural number, $G \in \mathfrak{S}$ and $E \in \rho^n\mathfrak{S}$ then

$$(G \cap E) \in \rho^n\mathfrak{S}.$$

Proof. (By induction on n).

Since it is well known that the intersection of an element of $\mathfrak{S}$ and an element of $\rho\mathfrak{S}$ is again an element of $\rho\mathfrak{S}$, the assertion is clear if $n = 1$.

Suppose next that the assertion is true for all natural numbers $\leq n - 1$. Let $\mathfrak{C}'$ be a subcollection of $\rho^{n-1}\mathfrak{S}$ which is centered in $G \cap E$. To prove that

$$(\cap\, \mathfrak{C}') \cap (G \cap E) \neq \emptyset,$$

we define

$$\mathfrak{C}'' = \{C \cap G \mid C \in \mathfrak{C}'\}.$$

By the induction hypothesis this collection is a subcollection of $\rho^{n-1}\mathfrak{S}$.

Since $\mathfrak{C}''$ is centered in E and $E \in \rho^n\mathfrak{S}$ it follows that

$$(\bigcap \mathfrak{C}'') \cap E \neq \emptyset,$$

$$\text{i.e. } (\bigcap \mathfrak{C}') \cap (G \cap E) \neq \emptyset.$$

Consequently

$$G \cap E \in \rho^n\mathfrak{S}.$$

Remark. Observe that from Alexander's lemma it follows that

$$(G \in \gamma\mathfrak{S}) \ \& \ (E \in \rho^n\mathfrak{S}) \Rightarrow (G \cap E \in \rho^n\mathfrak{S}),$$

since $\rho^n\gamma\mathfrak{S} = \rho^n\mathfrak{S}$ for every $\mathfrak{S}$.

2.10. Proposition. Let X be a (non-void) set and let $\mathfrak{S}$ be a collection of subsets of X.

If $E \in \rho^2\mathfrak{S}$ and $F \in \rho^3\mathfrak{S}$, then $E \cap F \in \rho\mathfrak{S}$.

Proof. Suppose that $E \in \rho^2\mathfrak{S}$ and $F \in \rho^3\mathfrak{S}$. If $\mathfrak{S}'$ is a subsystem of $\mathfrak{S}$ which is centered in $E \cap F$, then the system

$$\mathfrak{S}'' = \{S \cap E \mid S \in \mathfrak{S}'\}$$

is centered in F. $\mathfrak{S}''$ is a subsystem of $\rho^2\mathfrak{S}$ (cf. 2.9) and $F \in \rho^3\mathfrak{S}$. Thus we have

$$(\bigcap \mathfrak{S}') \cap (E \cap F) = (\bigcap \mathfrak{S}'') \cap F \neq \emptyset.$$

We conclude that $E \cap F$ is $\mathfrak{S}$-compact, which proves this proposition.

2.11. Corollary. For every set X and every collection $\mathfrak{S}$ of subsets of X we have

$$\rho^2\mathfrak{S} \cap \rho^3\mathfrak{S} = \rho\mathfrak{S} \cap \rho^2\mathfrak{S}.$$

Proof. Follows immediately from 2.6 and 2.10.

2.12. Remark. It is well known that a subset of a topological space is compact if and only if this set is compact in its relative topology. We can ask now whether or not this statement remains true when compact is replaced by squarecompact. We now give an example which shows that in general this is not true.

Example. Consider a sequence $\{p_i\}$ converging to a point p_0. In this sequence with the usual topology, all finite sets and all sets containing p_0 are closed, compact and squarecompact, whereas the set $\{p_i | i \neq 0\}$ is not squarecompact.

The subspace $\{p_i | i \neq 0\}$ is discrete in the relative topology. Therefore, every subset of this subspace, and in particular the set $\{p_i | i \neq 0\}$ itself, is squarecompact in this subspace.

3. A strengthening of Alexander's theorem

In this section we investigate the following question. Given a collection $\mathfrak{S}$ of subsets of a (non-empty) set X, which collections $\tilde{\mathfrak{S}}$ of subsets of X satisfy the conditions

$$\mathfrak{S} \subset \tilde{\mathfrak{S}} \quad \text{and} \quad \rho\mathfrak{S} = \rho\tilde{\mathfrak{S}}?$$

According to Alexander's theorem one can always take $\tilde{\mathfrak{S}} = \gamma\mathfrak{S}$.

We shall strengthen this result and give necessary and sufficient conditions which guarantee that there exists a maximal collection $\tilde{\mathfrak{S}}$ with the required properties.

3.1. Lemma. Let X be a set and let $\mathfrak{S}$ and $\mathfrak{T}$ be two collections of subsets of X. Then

$$\rho\mathfrak{S} \cap \rho\mathfrak{T} = \rho(\mathfrak{S} \cup \mathfrak{T})$$

if and only if for all C, $\tilde{S}$ and $\tilde{T}$

$$((C \in \rho\mathfrak{S} \cap \rho\mathfrak{T}) \;\&\; (\tilde{S} \in \gamma\mathfrak{S}) \;\&\; (\tilde{T} \in \gamma\mathfrak{T})) \Rightarrow$$

$$\Rightarrow ((C \cap \tilde{S} \in \rho\mathfrak{T}) \;\&\; (C \cap \tilde{T} \in \rho\mathfrak{S})).$$

Proof. To see the necessity,suppose first that there exist a set $\tilde{S} \in \gamma\mathfrak{S}$ and a set $C \in \rho\mathfrak{S} \cap \rho\mathfrak{T}$ such that

$$C \cap \tilde{S} \notin \rho\mathfrak{T}.$$

This means that $C \cap \tilde{S}$ is non-empty and that there exists a subfamily $\mathfrak{T}'$ of $\mathfrak{T}$ which is centered in $C \cap \tilde{S}$ and which has the property that

$$(\cap \mathfrak{T}') \cap (C \cap \tilde{S}) = \emptyset,$$

or equivalently $\quad ((\cap \mathfrak{T}') \cap \tilde{S}) \cap C = \emptyset.$

$\mathfrak{T}' \cup \{\tilde{S}\}$ is a subsystem of $\gamma(\mathfrak{S} \cup \mathfrak{T})$ which is centered in C and hence

$$C \notin \rho\gamma(\mathfrak{S} \cup \mathfrak{T}).$$

It follows from Alexander's theorem that

$$C \notin \rho(\mathfrak{S} \cup \mathfrak{T}).$$

Therefore

$$\rho(\mathfrak{S} \cup \mathfrak{T}) \neq \rho\mathfrak{S} \cap \rho\mathfrak{T}.$$

In the same way we can prove that if there exist a set $C \in \rho\mathfrak{S} \cap \rho\mathfrak{T}$ and a set $\tilde{T} \in \gamma\mathfrak{T}$ such that

$$\tilde{T} \cap C \notin \rho\mathfrak{S}$$

then we have that

$$\rho\mathfrak{S} \cap \rho\mathfrak{T} \neq \rho(\mathfrak{S} \cup \mathfrak{T}).$$

The two parts together prove the necessity of the condition.

To see the sufficiency, assume that for all C, $\tilde{S}$ and $\tilde{T}$ such that

$$C \in \rho\mathfrak{S} \cap \rho\mathfrak{T},\ \tilde{S} \in \gamma\mathfrak{S},\ \tilde{T} \in \gamma\mathfrak{T}$$

it is true that

$$C \cap \tilde{T} \in \rho\mathfrak{S} \quad \text{and} \quad C \cap \tilde{S} \in \rho\mathfrak{T}.$$

A set which is not a member of $\rho\mathfrak{S} \cap \rho\mathfrak{T}$ is either not $\mathfrak{S}$-compact or not $\mathfrak{T}$-compact and so clearly cannot be compact relative to $\mathfrak{S} \cup \mathfrak{T}$. This implies that

$$\text{(i)}\ \rho(\mathfrak{S} \cup \mathfrak{T}) \subset \rho\mathfrak{S} \cap \rho\mathfrak{T}.$$

To prove the opposite inclusion, assume that there exists a set C_0 which is a member of $\rho\mathfrak{T} \cap \rho\mathfrak{S}$ but not a member of $\rho(\mathfrak{S} \cup \mathfrak{T})$. Then there exists a system $\mathfrak{G} \subset \mathfrak{S} \cup \mathfrak{T}$ with the property that $\mathfrak{G}$ is centered in C_0, whereas

$$(\cap\, \mathfrak{G}) \cap C_0 = \emptyset.$$

We now define two disjoint subsystems of $\mathfrak{G}$ with union $\mathfrak{G}$ as follows:

$$\mathfrak{G}_s = \{G \mid G \in \mathfrak{G}\ \&\ G \notin \mathfrak{T}\}$$

and

$$\mathfrak{G}_t = \{G \mid G \in \mathfrak{G}\ \&\ G \in \mathfrak{T}\}.$$

Since

$$\mathfrak{G}_s \subset \mathfrak{S}$$

and since $\mathfrak{G}_s$ is centered in C_0, the fact that C_0 is $\mathfrak{S}$-compact implies that

$$C_s = (\cap\, \mathfrak{G}_s) \cap C_0 \neq \emptyset.$$

Since $C_0 \in \rho\mathfrak{T} \cap \rho\mathfrak{S}$ and

$$(\cap \mathfrak{G}_s) \in \gamma\mathfrak{S}$$

we have by assumption that

$$C_s \in \rho\mathfrak{T}.$$

Therefore, it follows from

$$\mathfrak{G}_t \subset \mathfrak{T}$$

and

$$(\cap \mathfrak{G}_t) \cap C_s = (\cap \mathfrak{G}_t) \cap (\cap \mathfrak{G}_s) \cap C_0 =$$

$$= (\cap \mathfrak{G}) \cap C_0 = \emptyset$$

that $\mathfrak{G}_t$ cannot be centered in C_s. Consequently, there exists a finite subsystem of $\mathfrak{G}_t$, call it

$$\{G_{ti} | i = 1, \ldots, n\},$$

such that

$$(\bigcap_{i=1}^{n} G_{ti}) \cap C_s = \emptyset.$$

Now let

$$C_t = (\bigcap_{i=1}^{n} G_{ti}) \cap C_0.$$

The set C_t cannot be empty, because $\mathfrak{G}$, and therefore $\mathfrak{G}_t$, is centered in C_0.

Since $C_0 \in \rho\mathfrak{S} \cap \rho\mathfrak{T}$ and $(\bigcap_{i=1}^{n} G_{ti}) \in \gamma\mathfrak{T}$, we have by assumption that

$$C_t \in \rho\mathfrak{S}.$$

Therefore it follows from

$$\mathfrak{G}_s \subset \mathfrak{S}$$

and

$$(\cap \mathfrak{G}_s) \cap C_t = (\cap \mathfrak{G}_s) \cap (\bigcap_{i=1}^{n} G_{ti}) \cap C_0 =$$

$$= (\bigcap_{i=1}^{n} G_{ti}) \cap C_s = \emptyset$$

that $\mathfrak{G}_s$ cannot be centered in C_t.
Consequently there exists a finite subsystem of $\mathfrak{G}_s$, call it

$$\{G_{sj} | j = 1, \ldots, m\},$$

such that

$$(\bigcap_{j=1}^{m} G_{sj}) \cap C_t = \emptyset.$$

It follows that

$$(\bigcap_{j=1}^{m} G_{sj}) \cap (\bigcap_{i=1}^{n} G_{ti}) \cap C_0 = \emptyset.$$

The system

$$\{G_{sj} | j = 1, \ldots, m\} \cup \{G_{ti} | i = 1, \ldots, n\}$$

is a finite subsystem of $\mathfrak{G}$ which has an empty intersection with C_0 and so $\mathfrak{G}$ is not centered in C_0. This is a contradiction.
We conclude that

$$\text{(ii)} \quad \rho\mathfrak{S} \cap \rho\mathfrak{T} \subset \rho(\mathfrak{S} \cup \mathfrak{T}).$$

From (i) and (ii) it follows that

$$\rho\mathfrak{S} \cap \rho\mathfrak{T} = \rho(\mathfrak{S} \cup \mathfrak{T}).$$

<u>3.2. Corollary</u>. If X is a set and $\mathfrak{S}$ and $\mathfrak{T}$ are two systems of subsets of X with the property that $\rho\mathfrak{S} = \rho\mathfrak{T}$, then

$$\rho(\mathfrak{S} \cup \mathfrak{T}) = \rho\mathfrak{S} = \rho\mathfrak{T}.$$

Proof. Let $C \in \rho\mathfrak{S} \cap \rho\mathfrak{T}$ $(= \rho\mathfrak{S} = \rho\mathfrak{T})$.
If $S \in \gamma\mathfrak{S}$, then

$$S \cap C \in \rho\mathfrak{T} = \rho\mathfrak{S}.$$

(The intersection of an $\mathfrak{S}$-closed set and an $\mathfrak{S}$-compact set is $\mathfrak{S}$-compact).

Similarly, if $T \in \gamma\mathfrak{T}$, then $T \cap C \in \rho\mathfrak{S} = \rho\mathfrak{T}$.
Thus the conditions of the preceding lemma are fulfilled. Hence

$$\rho(\mathfrak{S} \cup \mathfrak{T}) = \rho\mathfrak{S} \cap \rho\mathfrak{T} = \rho\mathfrak{S} = \rho\mathfrak{T}.$$

3.3. Remark. If $\{\mathfrak{S}_i\}_i$ is a finite collection of systems of subsets of a given set X such that

$$\rho\mathfrak{S}_i = \rho\mathfrak{S}_j \text{ for all } i \text{ and } j,$$

then it follows from the preceding corollary that

$$\rho(\bigcup_i \mathfrak{S}_i) = \rho\mathfrak{S}_j \text{ for all } j.$$

The question arises whether or not the same conclusion is valid for an infin collection $\{\mathfrak{S}_i\}_i$. We show by means of the following example that this need not be the case

Example. Let X be an infinite set. For every subset A of X we define a collection of subsets $\mathfrak{S}_A$ as follows:

$$\mathfrak{S}_A = \{A\} \cup \{\{p\} \mid p \in X\}.$$

Thus $\mathfrak{S}_A$ consists of the set A and all sets that contain exactly one point. Then $\rho\mathfrak{S}_A$ is the power-set of X and so

$$\rho\mathfrak{S}_A = \rho\mathfrak{S}_B \text{ for all } A \subset X \text{ and } B \subset X.$$

On the other hand, since it is also the case that

$$\cup \{\mathfrak{S}_A \mid A \subset X\}$$

is the power-set of X ,it follows that

$$\rho(\cup \{\mathfrak{S}_A \mid A \subset X\})$$

consists of all finite subsets of X and hence

$$\rho(\bigcup\{\mathfrak{S}_A \mid A \subset X\}) \neq \rho\mathfrak{S}_B \text{ for all } B \subset X.$$

We also show that there is no maximal collection of subsets of X with the property that every subset of X is compact relative to this collection. For, suppose that $\tilde{\mathfrak{S}}$ is a maximal collection of subsets such that $\rho\tilde{\mathfrak{S}}$ is the power set of X. Then $\tilde{\mathfrak{S}}$ cannot contain every subset of X and so there exists a subset A such that $A \not\in \tilde{\mathfrak{S}}$. Then the collection $\mathfrak{S}_A$ which is defined above has the property that $\rho\mathfrak{S}_A = \rho\tilde{\mathfrak{S}}$ and therefore

$$\rho(\tilde{\mathfrak{S}} \cup \mathfrak{S}_A) = \rho\tilde{\mathfrak{S}} \quad \text{(cf. 3.2)}.$$

This contradicts the assumption that $\tilde{\mathfrak{S}}$ is maximal. We conclude that for every infinite set X there are collections $\mathfrak{S}$ of subsets such that there does not exist a maximal collection $\tilde{\mathfrak{S}} \supset \mathfrak{S}$ with the property that $\rho\mathfrak{S} = \rho\tilde{\mathfrak{S}}$. (In the preceding example, take for instance $\mathfrak{S} = \emptyset$).

<u>3.4. Theorem</u>. Let X be a set. For every family $\mathfrak{S}$ of subsets of X we have

$$\rho\mathfrak{S} = \rho\gamma(\mathfrak{S} \cup \rho^2\mathfrak{S}).$$

Proof. In proposition 2.6 we found that $\rho\mathfrak{S} \subset \rho^3\mathfrak{S}$ or

$$\rho\mathfrak{S} \cap \rho(\rho^2\mathfrak{S}) = \rho\mathfrak{S}.$$

The intersection of a member of $\rho\mathfrak{S}$ and a member of $\gamma\mathfrak{S}$ is a member of $\rho\mathfrak{S}$ and hence a member of $\rho^3\mathfrak{S}$. Lemma 2.4 implies that the intersection of a member of $\gamma\rho^2\mathfrak{S}$ and a member of $\rho\mathfrak{S}$ is a member of $\rho\mathfrak{S}$ and therefore all conditions of 3.1 are fulfilled. It follows that

$$\rho(\mathfrak{S} \cup \rho^2\mathfrak{S}) = \rho\mathfrak{S} \cap \rho(\rho^2\mathfrak{S}) = \rho\mathfrak{S} \cap \rho^3\mathfrak{S} = \rho\mathfrak{S}.$$

An application of Alexander's theorem ($\rho\gamma = \rho$) yields the required results.

<u>Alternative proof</u>. This theorem can also be proved using the following

Lemma (P. Bacon).
If $\mathfrak{S}$ and $\mathfrak{T}$ are collections of subsets of a set X, then

$$\rho(\mathfrak{S} \cup \mathfrak{T}) = \rho\mathfrak{S} \cap \rho\mathfrak{T} \cap \rho(\{S \cap T | S \in \mathfrak{S} \ \& \ T \in \mathfrak{T}\}).$$

Proof. If $C \in \rho(\mathfrak{S} \cup \mathfrak{T})$, then C is $\mathfrak{S}$-compact and $\mathfrak{T}$-compact. Moreover, $C \in \rho\gamma(\mathfrak{S} \cup \mathfrak{T})$ and this implies that C is compact relative to the family consisting of all intersections of a member of $\mathfrak{S}$ with a member of $\mathfrak{T}$. We conclude that

$$\rho(\mathfrak{S} \cup \mathfrak{T}) \subset \rho\mathfrak{S} \cap \rho\mathfrak{T} \cap \rho(\{S \cap T | S \in \mathfrak{S} \ \& \ T \in \mathfrak{T}\}).$$

In order to prove the opposite inclusion we assume that

$$D \in \rho\mathfrak{S} \cap \rho\mathfrak{T} \cap \rho(\{S \cap T | S \in \mathfrak{S} \ \& \ T \in \mathfrak{T}\})$$

and that $\mathfrak{G}$ is a subsystem of $\mathfrak{S} \cup \mathfrak{T}$ which is centered in D. If $\mathfrak{G}$ consists merely of members of $\mathfrak{S}$ or merely of members of $\mathfrak{T}$, then from $D \in \rho\mathfrak{S} \cap \rho\mathfrak{T}$ it fo lows that $(\cap \mathfrak{G}) \cap D \neq \emptyset$. If $\mathfrak{G}$ consists of members of both $\mathfrak{S}$ and $\mathfrak{T}$, then we select $S_1 \in \mathfrak{S} \cap \mathfrak{G}$ and $T_1 \in \mathfrak{T} \cap \mathfrak{G}$. Then the system

$$\mathfrak{G}' = \{S_1 \cap G | G \in \mathfrak{G} \cap \mathfrak{T}\} \cup \{T_1 \cap G | G \in \mathfrak{G} \cap \mathfrak{S}\}$$

is a subsystem of

$$\{S \cap T | S \in \mathfrak{S} \ \& \ T \in \mathfrak{T}\},$$

which is centered in D and satisfies the equality

$$\cap \mathfrak{G}' = \cap \mathfrak{G}.$$

It follows that

$$(\cap \mathfrak{G}) \cap D = (\cap \mathfrak{G}') \cap D \neq \emptyset.$$

We conclude that in every case $(\cap \mathfrak{G}) \cap D \neq \emptyset$. Consequently

$$D \in \rho(\mathfrak{S} \cup \mathfrak{T})$$

and therefore

$$\rho(\mathfrak{S} \cup \mathfrak{T}) \supset \rho\mathfrak{S} \cap \rho\mathfrak{T} \cap \rho(\{S \cap T | S \in \mathfrak{S} \ \& \ T \in \mathfrak{T}\}).$$

This proves the lemma.

<u>Proof of theorem 3.4</u>. If we replace $\mathfrak{T}$ by $\rho^2\mathfrak{S}$, then we obtain

$$\rho(\mathfrak{S} \cup \rho^2\mathfrak{S}) = \rho\mathfrak{S} \cap \rho^3\mathfrak{S} \cap \rho(\{S \cap T | S \in \mathfrak{S} \,\&\, T \in \rho^2\mathfrak{S}\}).$$

Proposition 2.6 and proposition 2.9 imply that

$$\rho\mathfrak{S} \subset \rho^3\mathfrak{S} \subset \rho(\{S \cap T | S \in \mathfrak{S} \,\&\, T \in \rho^2\mathfrak{S}\}).$$

Hence we have

$$\rho(\mathfrak{S} \cup \rho^2\mathfrak{S}) = \rho\mathfrak{S}$$

and from Alexander's lemma it follows that

$$\rho\mathfrak{S} = \rho\gamma(\mathfrak{S} \cup \rho^2\mathfrak{S}).$$

<u>3.5. Remark</u>. This theorem can be seen as a strengthening of Alexander's theorem. The family $\tilde{\mathfrak{S}} = \gamma(\mathfrak{S} \cup \rho^2\mathfrak{S})$ contains the collection $\gamma\mathfrak{S}$ and all finite subsets of X. Moreover, at the end of this section we will prove that in many cases $\tilde{\mathfrak{S}}$ is the largest family of subsets of X with the property that $\rho\tilde{\mathfrak{S}} = \rho\mathfrak{S}$.

<u>3.6. Proposition</u>. For every collection of subsets $\mathfrak{S}$ of a set X, the following relation holds:

$$\rho(\mathfrak{S} \cup \rho\mathfrak{S}) = \rho\mathfrak{S} \cap \rho^2\mathfrak{S} = \rho(\rho\mathfrak{S} \cup \rho^2\mathfrak{S}) =$$

$$= \rho(\rho^2\mathfrak{S} \cup \rho^3\mathfrak{S}).$$

Proof. We first show that

$$\rho(\mathfrak{S} \cup \rho\mathfrak{S}) = \rho\mathfrak{S} \cap \rho^2\mathfrak{S},$$

then we show that the rest of the equalities follow from 2.11. From proposition 2.9 and Alexander's theorem it follows that the intersection of a member of $\gamma\mathfrak{S}$ with a member of $\rho^2\gamma\mathfrak{S} \cap \rho\gamma\mathfrak{S}$ is a member of $\rho^2\gamma\mathfrak{S}$, and hence

$$\text{(i)}: \{S \cap C \mid S \in \gamma\mathfrak{S} \ \&\ C \in (\rho^2\mathfrak{S} \cap \rho\mathfrak{S})\} \subset \rho^2\mathfrak{S}.$$

On the other hand, let D be a member of $\gamma\rho\mathfrak{S}$ and let E be a member of $\rho^2\mathfrak{S} \cap \rho\mathfrak{S}$. Then there is a system of sets $\mathfrak{C} \subset \rho\mathfrak{S}$ such that $\bigcap \mathfrak{C} = D$. If $C \in \mathfrak{C}$, then $C \cap E \in \rho^2\mathfrak{S}$ by lemma 2.4, and therefore

$$D \cap E = (\bigcap \{C \cap E \mid C \in \mathfrak{C}\}) \in \rho^2\mathfrak{S}$$

by theorem 2.5. Let C_1 be an arbitrary member of $\mathfrak{C}$, then $C_1 \in \rho\mathfrak{S}$, and from lemma 2.4 it follows that

$$D \cap E = C_1 \cap (D \cap E) \in \rho\mathfrak{S}.$$

Consequently

$$\text{(ii)}: \{D \cap E \mid D \in \rho\gamma\mathfrak{S} \ \&\ E \in \rho\mathfrak{S} \cap \rho^2\mathfrak{S}\} \subset \rho\mathfrak{S}.$$

From (i), (ii) and lemma 3.1 we conclude that

$$\rho(\mathfrak{S} \cup \rho\mathfrak{S}) = \rho\mathfrak{S} \cap \rho^2\mathfrak{S}.$$

Now if we apply this equality to $\rho\mathfrak{S}$ we find

$$\rho(\rho\mathfrak{S} \cup \rho^2\mathfrak{S}) = \rho^2\mathfrak{S} \cap \rho^3\mathfrak{S} = \rho\mathfrak{S} \cap \rho^2\mathfrak{S} \quad \text{(cf. 2.11)}.$$

Moreover, applying the same equality to $\rho^2\mathfrak{S}$ yields

$$\rho(\rho^2\mathfrak{S} \cup \rho^3\mathfrak{S}) = \rho^3\mathfrak{S} \cap \rho^4\mathfrak{S} =$$

$$= \rho^3\mathfrak{S} \cap \rho^2\mathfrak{S} = \rho\mathfrak{S} \cap \rho^2\mathfrak{S}.$$

This proves the proposition.

The following proposition deals with the problem of determining conditions on a set X and a collection of subsets $\mathfrak{S}$ which guarantee that there exists a maximal family $\tilde{\mathfrak{S}}$ with the property that $\rho\mathfrak{S} = \rho\tilde{\mathfrak{S}}$. From proposition 3.2 it is clear that if $\tilde{\mathfrak{S}}$ is such a maximal family, then $\mathfrak{S} \subset \tilde{\mathfrak{S}}$, and the family $\tilde{\mathfrak{S}}$ is the only maximal family, so the greatest, with $\rho\tilde{\mathfrak{S}} = \rho\mathfrak{S}$.

<u>3.7. Proposition</u>. Let X be a set and let $\mathfrak{S}$ be a collection of subsets of X. If we define

$$\mathfrak{T} = \{A | A \subset X \ \& \ (\forall C \in \rho\mathfrak{S})(A \cap C \in \rho\mathfrak{S})\},$$

then a necessary and sufficient condition for the existence of a maximal family $\tilde{\mathfrak{S}}$ with the property that $\rho\tilde{\mathfrak{S}} = \rho\mathfrak{S}$ is that $\rho\mathfrak{T} = \rho\mathfrak{S}$. In this case $\tilde{\mathfrak{S}} = \mathfrak{T}$.

Proof. To see the necessity, suppose that there exists a maximal family $\tilde{\mathfrak{S}}$ with the property that $\rho\mathfrak{S} = \rho\tilde{\mathfrak{S}}$. We prove that $\mathfrak{T} = \tilde{\mathfrak{S}}$ and $\rho\mathfrak{S} = \rho\mathfrak{T}$.

Let $T \in \mathfrak{T}$. Then $\{T\}$ is a collection of subsets of X and every subset of X is compact relative to $\{T\}$. It follows easily that

$$\rho\tilde{\mathfrak{S}} \cap \rho\{T\} = \rho\tilde{\mathfrak{S}} = \rho\mathfrak{S}.$$

Let C_0 be a member of $\rho\tilde{\mathfrak{S}}$ and let S_0 be a member of $\gamma\tilde{\mathfrak{S}}$. Clearly

$$C_0 \cap S_0 \in \rho\{T\}.$$

Since $T \in \mathfrak{T}$ we also have

$$C_0 \cap T \in \rho\mathfrak{S} = \rho\tilde{\mathfrak{S}}.$$

Hence we may apply lemma 3.1 to obtain

$$\rho(\tilde{\mathfrak{S}} \cup \{T\}) = \rho\tilde{\mathfrak{S}} \cap \rho\{T\} = \rho\tilde{\mathfrak{S}} = \rho\mathfrak{S}.$$

From the assumption that $\tilde{\mathfrak{S}}$ is maximal it follows that $T \in \tilde{\mathfrak{S}}$ and hence

$$\mathfrak{T} \subset \tilde{\mathfrak{S}}.$$

Now we suppose that there exists an $S_0 \in \tilde{\mathfrak{S}}$ such that $S_0 \notin \mathfrak{T}$. Then by definition of $\mathfrak{T}$ there exists a set $C_0 \in \rho\mathfrak{S}$ such that

$$S_0 \cap C_0 \notin \rho\mathfrak{S}.$$

From this it is easy to see that $C_0 \notin \rho\tilde{\mathfrak{S}}$ which contradicts the assumption that $\rho\mathfrak{S} = \rho\tilde{\mathfrak{S}}$. We conclude that $\tilde{\mathfrak{S}} \subset \mathfrak{T}$.
Therefore $\mathfrak{T} = \tilde{\mathfrak{S}}$ and $\rho\mathfrak{T} = \rho\tilde{\mathfrak{S}} = \rho\mathfrak{S}$.

To see the sufficiency, suppose that $\rho\mathfrak{S} = \rho\mathfrak{T}$. We will prove that $\mathfrak{T}$ contains every system $\mathfrak{S}'$ with the property that $\rho\mathfrak{S}' = \rho\mathfrak{S}$. Suppose that S' is a member of such a system $\mathfrak{S}'$. Then

$$(S' \cap C') \in \rho\mathfrak{S}' \text{ for every } C' \in \rho\mathfrak{S}'.$$

Since $\rho\mathfrak{S}' = \rho\mathfrak{S}$ we have by definition $S' \in \mathfrak{T}$. This proves that $\mathfrak{T}$ contains every system $\mathfrak{S}'$ with $\rho\mathfrak{S} = \rho\mathfrak{S}'$ and so $\mathfrak{T}$ is the unique maximal collection of subsets of X with the property that it has the same collection of compact sets as $\mathfrak{S}$. This proves the proposition.

3.8. Theorem. Let X be a set. For any collection $\mathfrak{S}$ of subsets of X we have that

$$(\rho\mathfrak{S} \subset \rho^2\mathfrak{S}) \Rightarrow (\mathfrak{S} \subset \rho^2\mathfrak{S}).$$

Moreover, these conditions imply that

$$\rho^2\mathfrak{S} = \{A \mid (\forall C \in \rho\mathfrak{S})(C \cap A \in \rho\mathfrak{S})\}.$$

Proof. Since $\rho\mathfrak{S} \subset \rho^2\mathfrak{S}$, every centered subsystem of $\rho\mathfrak{S}$ has a non-empty intersection. It follows that $X \in \rho^2\mathfrak{S}$ and proposition 2.9 implies that $\mathfrak{S} \subset \rho^2\mathfrak{S}$.

If we put

$$\mathfrak{T} = \{A \mid (\forall C \in \rho\mathfrak{S})(A \cap C \in \rho\mathfrak{S})\},$$

then we must prove that $\rho^2\mathfrak{S} = \mathfrak{T}$. Lemma 2.4 implies that every member of $\rho^2\mathfrak{S}$ is a member of $\mathfrak{T}$.

Conversely, let $T \in \mathfrak{T}$. Since every centered subsystem of $\rho\mathfrak{S}$ has a non-empty intersection,it follows easily that every subsystem of $\rho\mathfrak{S}$ which is centered in T has a non-empty intersection with T. This proves that $T \in \rho^2\mathfrak{S}$ and so $\mathfrak{T} = \rho^2\mathfrak{S}$.

Finally,we remark that 3.4 implies that in this case $\rho\mathfrak{S} = \rho^3\mathfrak{S}$.

Theorem 3.8 and proposition 3.7 show that there are families of subsets $\mathfrak{S}$ such that the family derived in 3.4 is maximal with respect to the properties of containing $\mathfrak{S}$ and having the same compact sets as $\mathfrak{S}$. It is easy to see that the conditions of theorem 3.8 are fulfilled for every closed subbase of a space in which compact implies closed, in particular a Hausdorff space.

Chapter II

Antispaces

This chapter is mainly concerned with establishing and investigating a one to one correspondence between two classes of antispaces. This one to one correspondence is based on two equalities of the previous chapter, i.e. $\gamma\rho^2 = \rho^2$ and $\rho^4 = \rho^2$. For our purposes it is more convenient to consider minusspaces (cf. def. 2.1) rather than topological spaces. In particular we consider those minusspaces in which the collection of squarecompact subsets coincides with the collection of closed subsets of the space and we call such a space an antispace. There exists a natural one to one mapping from the class of antispaces onto itself which assigns to every antispace another space on the same set in which the collection of compact subsets of the original space coincides with the collection of closed subsets of the second space.

The most important class of antispaces is the class of topological antispaces or C-spaces which is closely related to the class of compactly generated spaces.

We give a survey of the theory of C-spaces in the first section.

In the second section we introduce the notion of an antispace and establish the correspondence between C-spaces and compact antispaces (also called C^*-spaces), together with some basic properties.

The third section is devoted to subspaces and sumspaces of C-spaces and C^*-spaces. In this section we also introduce the notion of an antisubspace, which enables us to characterize the class of all antispaces.

1. C-spaces

1.1. Definition. A topological space $(X,\mathfrak{T})$ is called a C-space provided that a subset of the space is closed iff it has a compact intersection with every closed compact subset of the space.

A topological space is called a CC-space provided that every compact subset of the space is closed.

Observe that every Hausdorff space is a CC-space.

The definition of a C-space is closely related to the well known definitions of a k-space and of a compactly generated space (cf. [3], [4], [9] p. 5). A topological space is called a k-space provided that a subset in the space is closed iff it has a closed intersection with every closed compact subset of the space. A Hausdorff k-space is called a compactly generated space.

1.2. Proposition. A topological space X is a C-space if and only if it is a CC-space and a k-space.

Proof. Let X be a C-space. If C_0 is a compact subset of X, then it has a compact intersection with every closed compact set and so is closed. It follows that X is a CC-space.

If A is a subset of X which has a closed intersection with every closed compact subset of X, then it has a compact intersection with every closed compact subset of X and hence is closed. This means that X is a k-space.

Conversely, let X be a CC-k-space and let A be a subset of X which has a compact intersection with every closed compact subset of the space. Then from the fact that X is a CC-space it follows that A has a closed intersection with every closed compact subset of the space. Then A is closed, because X is a k-space. This proves that X is a C-space.

1.3. Proposition. A CC-space which satisfies the first axiom of countability is a Hausdorff C-space (compare with [7] p. 231 and [9] p. 5, 6).

Proof. Let X be a first countable CC-space and suppose that p and q are two points of the space that have no disjoint neighbourhoods.

Let

$$\{U_i \mid i \in N\}$$

be a countable neighbourhoodbase at p such that $U_{i+1} \subset U_i$ and let

$$\{V_i \mid i \in N\}$$

be such a neighbourhoodbase at q. We choose a sequence of points $\{x_i \mid i \in N\}$ such that $x_i \in V_i \cap U_i$ and $p \neq x_i \neq q$. This sequence converges to both p and q, and hence $\{x_i\} \cup \{p\}$ is not closed. However, $\{x_i\}_{i \in N} \cup \{p\}$ is compact. This is a contradiction, since X is a CC-space. It follows that X is a Hausdorff space.

Let A be a non-closed subset of X. Then there exist an accumulation point p of A which does not belong to A and a sequence $\{p_i \mid i \in N\}$ in A which converges to p. Then $\{p_i\} \cup \{p\}$ is compact and hence closed but its intersection with A is not compact. It follows that there exists a closed compact subset of X which has a non-compact intersection with A. Therefore, X must be a C-space.

<u>1.4. Proposition</u>. A locally compact CC-space is a C-space (compare with [9], p. 5, 6 and [7] p. 231).

Proof. Suppose that X is a locally compact CC-space and that A is a subset of the space such that $A \cap C$ is compact for every closed compact set C. If p is a point of the space which is not a member of A, then p has a compact neighbourhood C_p which is closed since X is a CC-space. By assumption $A \cap C_p$ is closed and does not contain p, which implies that $C_p \setminus A$ is still a neighbourhood of p. Hence p is not an accumulation point of A and it follows that A contains all of its accumulation points. Therefore A is closed and X is a C-space.

<u>1.5. Corollary</u>. Every compact CC-space is a C-space.

In a compact CC-space, the collection of closed sets coincides with the collection of compact sets. Therefore every strictly coarser topology on the underlying set cannot be CC and every strictly finer topology fails to be compact. We now introduce the notion of maximal compactness and prove that a space is maximal compact if and only if it is compact CC (cf. [8], [3]).

1.6. Definition. A topological space $(X,\mathfrak{T})$ is called maximal compact provided that X is compact relative to the topology $\mathfrak{T}$, but fails to be compact in every strictly finer topology.

1.7. Proposition. A topological space $(X,\mathfrak{T})$ is maximal compact if and only if it is compact CC (cf. [8]).

Proof. Suppose that $(X,\mathfrak{T})$ is maximal compact, and let C be an arbitrary compact subset of $(X,\mathfrak{T})$. In order to prove that C is closed, we suppose that $\mathfrak{G}'$ is a subsystem of the collection of closed subsets of $(X,\mathfrak{T})$ such that $\mathfrak{G}' \cup \{C\}$ is centered. Then

$$(\cap \mathfrak{G}') \cap C \neq \emptyset.$$

If we denote the collection of closed sets by $\mathfrak{G}$, then X is compact relative to $\mathfrak{G}$, to $\mathfrak{G} \cup \{C\}$ and also to $\gamma(\mathfrak{G} \cup \{C\})$. This collection $\gamma(\mathfrak{G} \cup \{C\})$ is the collection of closed subsets of a topology on X which is finer than (or equal to) the topology $\mathfrak{T}$. From the assumption that $(X,\mathfrak{T})$ is maximal compact it follows that $\mathfrak{G} = \gamma(\mathfrak{G} \cup \{C\})$ and so $C \in \mathfrak{G}$.

We conclude that every maximal compact space is a compact CC-space.

Conversely, we have seen in 1.5 that every compact CC-space is a maximal compact space.

1.8. Proposition. The one point compactification of a C-space is a maximal compact space.

Proof. Let $(X,\mathfrak{T})$ be a non-compact C-space and let p be a point which is not a member of X. Now we define the topology $\mathfrak{T}^*$ on $X \cup \{p\}$ in the usual way. $\mathfrak{T}^*$ contains every set of $\mathfrak{T}$, and the complements of closed compact subsets of X. Of course $(X \cup \{p\}, \mathfrak{T}^*)$ is compact.

In order to prove that $(X \cup \{p\}, \mathfrak{T}^*)$ is a CC-space we suppose that C is a compact subset of $(X \cup \{p\}, \mathfrak{T}^*)$. If $C \subset X$, then it is closed in $(X \cup \{p\}, \mathfrak{T}^*)$ by definition. Therefore we suppose that $p \in C$. Let D be an arbitrary closed compact subset of $(X,\mathfrak{T})$. If $C \cap D$ is empty, then $C \cap D$ is compact in $(X,\mathfrak{T})$. If $C \cap D \neq \emptyset$ then we suppose that $\mathfrak{G}'$ is a subsystem of the collection of closed subsets of $(X,\mathfrak{T})$ which is centered in $C \cap D$. Then the system

$$\mathfrak{G}'' = \{G \cup \{p\} \mid G \in \mathfrak{G}'\}$$

is a subcollection of the collection of closed sets in $(X \cup \{p\}, \mathfrak{T}^*)$ and it is also centered in $C \cap D$. Since X is a C-space D is closed and C is compact in $(X \cup \{p\}, \mathfrak{T}^*)$. It follows that

$$(\cap \mathfrak{G}'') \cap C \cap D \neq \emptyset.$$

The set D does not contain the point p since it is a subset of X and so

$$(\cap \mathfrak{G}') \cap (C \setminus \{p\}) \cap D \neq \emptyset.$$

Therefore, in both cases, if $C \cap D \neq \emptyset$ or if $C \cap D = \emptyset$, we have that $(C \setminus \{p\}) \cap D$ is compact in $(X,\mathfrak{T})$. Hence the set $C \setminus \{p\}$ has a compact intersection with every closed compact subset of $(X,\mathfrak{T})$. It follows that $C \setminus \{p\}$ is closed in $(X,\mathfrak{T})$ and thus C is closed in $(X \cup \{p\}, \mathfrak{T}^*)$. We conclude that $(X \cup \{p\}, \mathfrak{T}^*)$ is a compact CC-space which proves the proposition (cf. 1.7).

<u>1.9. Remark</u>. The preceding proposition shows that the class of C-spaces is not merely a class containing all locally compact Hausdorff spaces, but also a generalization of this class, since every member of the class has a one point compactification within the class. Moreover, it follows from 1.3 that every metrizable space is a C-space.

Every C-space is completely determined by its collection of compact sets. This property suggests that there is a relationship between the compactness operator and the class of C-spaces, and also a relationship with the class of compactly generated spaces.

Finally we observe that the class of maximal compact spaces can be considered as a generalization of the class of compact Hausdorff spaces, since in both classes the collection of compact subsets coincides with the collection of closed subsets and in both classes every one to one continuous function from a member of the class into a member of the class is a homeomorphism.

1.10. Proposition. Let Y be a subspace of the C-space X If Y is open or closed in the topology of X, then Y is a C-space (compare with [1]).

Proof. Let Y be a closed subset of X and let A be a subset of Y which has a compact intersection with every closed compact subset of Y. Then A has also a compact intersection with every closed compact subset of X and hence A is closed in X. This implies that A is closed in Y and so Y is a C-space.

Suppose that Y is open in X and that G_0 is the complement of Y in X. Let A be a subset of Y which has a compact intersection with every closed compact subset of Y. In order to prove that A is closed in Y it suffices to prove that $A \cup G_0$ is closed in X.

Suppose that $A \cup G_0$ is not closed in X. Then there exists a closed compact subset C_0 of X such that

$$(A \cup G_0) \cap C_0$$

is not compact. Therefore there exists a system of closed sets $\mathfrak{G}'$ in X which is centered in $(A \cup G_0) \cap C_0$ and such that

$$(\cap \mathfrak{G}') \cap (A \cup G_0) \cap C_0 = \emptyset.$$

Since G_0 is closed and C_0 is compact, $G_0 \cap C_0$ is a compact subset of X and, therefore, there exists a finite subsystem of $\mathfrak{G}'$,

$$\{G_i \mid i = 1, 2, \ldots, n\},$$

with the property that

$$\left(\bigcap_{i=1}^{n} G_i \right) \cap C_0 \cap G_0 = \emptyset.$$

If we define

$$C_2 = \left(\bigcap_{i=1}^{n} G_i \right) \cap C_0,$$

then clearly C_2 is a closed compact subset of Y. Then by assumption the set $A \cap C_2$ is compact. On the other hand, it follows easily that $\mathfrak{G}'$ is centered in $A \cap C_2$, whereas

$$(\cap \mathfrak{G}') \cap A \cap C_2 = (\cap \mathfrak{G}') \cap (A \cup G_0) \cap C_0 = \emptyset .$$

This is a contradiction which shows that $A \cup G_0$ is closed in X. Therefore A is closed in Y and so Y must be a C-space. This proves the theorem.

2. Minusspaces and antispaces

2.1. Definition. An ordered pair $(X,\mathfrak{G})$ consisting of a set X and a collection $\mathfrak{G}$ of subsets of X is called a minusspace iff $\gamma\mathfrak{G} = \mathfrak{G}$ (i.e. the collection $\mathfrak{G}$ is closed under the forming of finite unions and arbitrary intersections of non-empty subfamilies of $\mathfrak{G}$. $\mathfrak{G}$ is called a minustopology for X. The members of $\mathfrak{G}$ are called the closed subsets of $(X,\mathfrak{G})$ and the complements of members of $\mathfrak{G}$ are called open subsets of the minusspace. Observe that $(X,\gamma\mathfrak{S})$ is a minusspace for every collection $\mathfrak{S}$ of subsets of X.

2.2. Remark. In the sequel a "space" will mean a "minusspace". However, if confusion with "topological space" is likely, we will use the words minusspace or topological space. Recall that in a minusspace it is not necessary that the empty set and the entire set are closed. This is a consequence of the definition of the operator γ. In the following we shall occasionally use notions such as "subspace", "homeomorphism", "continuous function", "quotient space" when we deal with minusspaces. The definitions of these notions are completely analogous to the corresponding definitions for topological spaces and so we shall not formulate them explicitly. The definitions of C-space, CC-space, etc. for minusspaces are precisely the same as the definitions for topological C-spaces, resp.,CC-spaces; we merely have to replace the word topological space by minusspace. The definition of a minusspace is equivalent to the definition of a topological space for many classes of spaces that are usually studied. If a space contains two disjoint closed sets,then the empty set is closed and if a space contains two disjoint open sets,then the entire set is closed. Every C-minusspace is a topological space because both the empty set and the entire set have a compact intersection with every closed compact set and hence they must be closed.

Every topological space is a minusspace and every minusspace can be changed into a topological space by the adjunction of the empty set and the entire set to the collection of closed subsets. Almost every theorem for topological spaces, resp., for minusspaces can be reformulated for minusspaces, resp., for topological spaces with occasionally a comment on the empty set and the entire set.

If we define the closure of a set A to be the set of all points p such that every open set which contains p intersects A, then the notion of a minusspace has the disadvantage that the closure of a set in the space need not be closed. Indeed, the closure of a set is not closed if and only if the set is dense (i.e., every non-empty open subset intersects it) and the entire set is not closed. Observe that in this case the closure of a set is not the intersection of all closed sets containing the given set.

We now reformulate theorem 1.2.5 in the following way:

2.3. Theorem. If X is a set and if $\mathfrak{S}$ is a collection of subsets of X, then $\rho^2\mathfrak{S}$ is a collection of closed sets in a minusspace on X.

2.4. Definition. An unordered pair of minusspaces on the same set $\{(X,\mathfrak{G}_1),(X,\mathfrak{G}_2)\}$ is called an antipair if and only if $\mathfrak{G}_2 = \rho\mathfrak{G}_1$ and $\mathfrak{G}_1 = \rho\mathfrak{G}_2$. A member of an antipair is called an antispace and if $\{(X,\mathfrak{G}_1),(X,\mathfrak{G}_2)\}$ is an antipair, then $(X,\mathfrak{G}_1)$ is called the anti-image of $(X,\mathfrak{G}_2)$ and conversely.

2.5. Remark. From the definition it follows that $(X,\mathfrak{G})$ is an antispace if and only if $\rho^2\mathfrak{G} = \mathfrak{G}$ and, in this case, the unordered pair $\{(X,\mathfrak{G}),(X,\rho\mathfrak{G})\}$ is an antipair. By definition this is the only antipair which contains $(X,\mathfrak{G})$ and so every antispace $(X,\mathfrak{G})$ has a unique anti-image, i.e., $(X,\rho\mathfrak{G})$. Observe that $\emptyset \in \mathfrak{G}$ for every antispace $(X,\mathfrak{G})$.

2.6. Theorem. If $(X,\mathfrak{G})$ is an arbitrary minusspace, then $(X,\rho^2\mathfrak{G})$ is an antispace and its anti-image is $(X,\rho^3\mathfrak{G})$.

Proof. Follows immediately from theorem I.2.7 and the preceding remark.

This theorem remains valid for every set X and every collection of subsets $\mathfrak{S}$, i.e., $(X,\rho^2\mathfrak{S})$ is an antispace and its anti-image is $(X,\rho^3\mathfrak{S})$. This follows from I.1.9.

2.7. Definition. A minusspace $(X,\mathfrak{G})$ is called compact provided that $X \in \rho\mathfrak{G}$. A compact antispace is called a C^*-space.

2.8. Theorem. For every minusspace $(X,\mathfrak{G})$ the following statements are equivalent.

(i) $(X,\mathfrak{G})$ is a C-space.

(ii) $(X,\mathfrak{G})$ is a topological space and an antispace.

(iii) There exists a C^*-space $(X,\mathfrak{K})$ such that $\rho\mathfrak{K} = \mathfrak{G}$.

(iv) $(X,\mathfrak{G})$ is a CC-antispace.

Proof. The pattern of proof is (i) ⇒ (ii) ⇒ (iii) ⇒ (iv) ⇒ (i).

(i) ⇒ (ii). Suppose that $(X,\mathfrak{G})$ is a C-space. Then it is a topological space (cf. 2.2). Every compact subset of the space is closed (cf. 1.2) and so every centered system of compact sets has a non-empty intersection, which implies that the set X itself is squarecompact. From I.2.9 it follows that every closed set is squarecompact, i.e. $\mathfrak{G} \subset \rho^2\mathfrak{G}$.

In order to prove that every squarecompact set is closed, we take any squarecompact set A. It follows from I.2.4 that A has a compact intersection with every compact (and hence closed) subset of $(X,\mathfrak{G})$. A is closed since $(X,\mathfrak{G})$ is a C-space. This implies that every squarecompact subset of $(X,\mathfrak{G})$ is closed. We conclude that $(X,\mathfrak{G})$ is a topological antispace.

(ii) ⇒ (iii). Suppose that $(X,\mathfrak{G})$ is a topological antispace. Then $(X,\rho\mathfrak{G})$ is also an antispace, and from $X \in \mathfrak{G} = \rho^2\mathfrak{G}$ it follows that $(X,\rho\mathfrak{G})$ is a compact antispace, i.e. a C^*-space and $(X,\mathfrak{G})$ is the anti-image of this C^*-space.

(iii) ⇒ (iv). Let $(X,\mathfrak{K})$ be a compact antispace with the property that $\mathfrak{G} = \rho\mathfrak{K}$. Then $(X,\mathfrak{G})$ is an antispace (cf. 2.5). $(X,\mathfrak{K})$ is a compact antispace which implies that $\mathfrak{K} \subset \rho\mathfrak{K} = \mathfrak{G}$. Therefore $\rho\mathfrak{G} = \mathfrak{K} \subset \mathfrak{G}$, which means that $(X,\mathfrak{G})$ is a CC-space. This proves that $(X,\mathfrak{G})$ is a CC-antispace.

(iv) ⇒ (i). Suppose that $(X,\mathfrak{G})$ is a CC-antispace and suppose that A is a subset of X which has a compact intersection with every compact subset of $(X,\mathfrak{G})$. Let $\mathfrak{C}'$ be a system of compact subsets which is centered in A, and let C_0 be a member of $\mathfrak{C}'$. Then $\mathfrak{C}'$ can be considered as a system of closed sets which is centered in $C_0 \cap A$. The set $C_0 \cap A$ is compact and therefore

$$(\bigcap \mathfrak{C}') \cap A = (\bigcap \mathfrak{C}') \cap C_0 \cap A \neq \emptyset.$$

This implies that A is squarecompact and hence A is closed. It follows that $(X,\mathfrak{G})$ is a C-space.

2.9. Remark. From this theorem it follows that the class of C-spaces is closely related to the class of C^*-spaces. There exists a well defined one to one correspondence between these classes, namely, every C^*-space is the anti-image of one and only one C-space and conversely. Every antispace determines its anti-image completely and therefore every property of the anti-image corresponds to some property of the original antispace. The topology on a C-space is (not necessary strictly) finer than the minus-topology on the corresponding C^*-space because the identity function is continuous.

It is easy to see that a space is maximal compact if and only if it is both a C-space and a C^*-space. (Observe that a maximal compact space is a compact antispace.) In this case the space is the anti-image of itself and its antipair consists of two identical spaces.

It seems reasonable to ask if every antispace is a C-space or a C^*-space. The answer to this question is in the negative. It is even possible to find an antipair consisting of two homeomorphic minusspaces such that neither is a C-space. We show this in the following example.

Example. Let X be the set of real numbers and let $\mathfrak{G}$ be the collection of all subsets of X which are bounded to the left and closed in the usual real-line topology.It is easy to see that $(X,\mathfrak{G})$ is a minusspace. A subset A of $(X,\mathfrak{G})$ is a member of $\rho\mathfrak{G}$ if and only if it is bounded to the right and closed in the usual topology on X. Therefore $\{(X,\mathfrak{G}),(X,\rho\mathfrak{G})\}$ is an antipair consisting of two homeomorphic spaces. Clearly, neither is a C-space, since every C-space is a topological space.

2.10. Proposition. If $(X,\mathfrak{G})$ is a CC-space, then $(X,\rho\mathfrak{G})$ is a C^*-space.

Proof. By definition $\rho\mathfrak{G} \subset \mathfrak{G}$ and hence $\rho\mathfrak{G} \subset \rho^2\mathfrak{G}$. Therefore $X \in \rho^2\mathfrak{G}$, since every centered subsystem of $\rho\mathfrak{G}$ has a non-void intersection. Now theorem I.3.8 implies that $\mathfrak{G} \subset \rho^2\mathfrak{G}$ and from I.3.4 it follows that $\rho\mathfrak{G} = \rho^3\mathfrak{G}$. We conclude that $(X,\rho\mathfrak{G})$ is a compact antispace, which proves the proposition.

2.11. Proposition. If $(X,\rho^2\mathfrak{G})$ is a C-space, then $(X,\rho\mathfrak{G})$ is a C^*-space.

Proof. $(X,\rho^2\mathfrak{G})$ is a C-space and hence a CC-space. This implies that $\rho^2\mathfrak{G} \supset \rho^3\mathfrak{G} \supset \rho\mathfrak{G}$ (cf. I.2.6). We may apply again I.3.8 and I.3.4 and the proposition can be proved in the same way as the preceding proposition.

2.12. Theorem. If $(X,\mathfrak{G})$ is an arbitrary minusspace, then $(X,\rho\mathfrak{G} \cap \rho^2\mathfrak{G})$ is a C^*-space.

Proof. Clearly $(X,\gamma(\mathfrak{G} \cup \rho\mathfrak{G}))$ is a CC-minusspace and from I.3.6 it follows that $\rho\mathfrak{G} \cap \rho^2\mathfrak{G}$ is its collection of compact subsets. Now the theorem follows from 2.10.

2.13. Corollary. If $(X,\mathfrak{G})$ is an arbitrary minusspace, then $(X,\rho(\rho\mathfrak{G} \cap \rho^2\mathfrak{G}))$ is a C-space.

2.14. Remark. It is well known that for every Hausdorff space $(X,\mathfrak{T})$ there exists a uniquely defined k-space $(X,\tilde{\mathfrak{T}})$ with the same collection of compact sets (cf. [7] p. 241, [1]). $(X,\mathfrak{T})$ is the image of $(X,\tilde{\mathfrak{T}})$ under a one-to-one continuous mapping. We shall call $(X,\tilde{\mathfrak{T}})$ the k-expansion of $(X,\mathfrak{T})$. This k-expansion is usually defined in the following equivalent way:
If $(X,\mathfrak{T})$ is a (topological) Hausdorff space, and $\mathfrak{G}$ is its collection of closed sets, then we define the k-expansion as the topological space which has the collection

$$\tilde{\mathfrak{G}} = \{A \mid (\forall\, C \in \rho\mathfrak{G})(A \cap C \in \mathfrak{G})\}$$

as its collection of closed sets. It is easy to see that the k-expansion of any Hausdorff space is a C-space.

The preceding corollary now suggests the following definition of the C-expansion $(X,\tilde{\mathfrak{G}})$ of any minusspace $(X,\mathfrak{G})$:

$$\tilde{\mathfrak{G}} = \rho(\rho\mathfrak{G} \cap \rho^2\mathfrak{G}).$$

It follows that the identity mapping from $(X,\tilde{\mathfrak{G}})$ to $(X,\mathfrak{G})$ is continuous. Furthermore, if $(X,\mathfrak{G})$ is a CC-space, or even if $(X,\rho\mathfrak{G})$ is a C^*-space, then $\rho\mathfrak{G}$ and $\rho\tilde{\mathfrak{G}}$ are identical collections of sets (cf. I.3.8). It is easy to see that if the k-expansion of a topological space is defined, then it coincides with the C-expansion.

3. Subspaces and sumspaces of antispaces

In this section we study the one-to-one correspondence between the class of C-spaces and the class of C^*-spaces which we found in 2.9. We will prove theorems in the theory of C^*-spaces with correspond to theorem 1.8 and 1.10 in the theory of C-spaces. In the theory of C^*-spaces we will define the notion of an antisubspace which corresponds to the notion of a (topological) subspace in the theory of C-spaces. We show that the correspondence between C-spaces and C^*-spaces is not entirely invariant under the taking of subspaces and antisubspaces. The notion of an antisubspace is also useful for the investigation of minusspaces in general. For example, we shall give a characterization of the class of antispaces which is based on the notion of an antisubspace.

3.1. Definition. A minusspace $(X,\mathfrak{G})$ is an antisubspace of the minusspace $(Y,\mathfrak{S})$ iff $X \subset Y$ and

$$\mathfrak{G} = \{G \mid G \subset X \ \& \ G \in \mathfrak{S}\}.$$

$\mathfrak{G}$ is called the anti-relative minustopology on X and the identity mapping from $(X,\mathfrak{G})$ into $(Y,\mathfrak{S})$ is called an anti-embedding.

Remark. Observe that the relative minustopology on X is defined, as usual, by

$$\mathfrak{G} = \{X \cap S \mid S \in \mathfrak{S}\}.$$

In this case $(X,\mathfrak{G})$ is called a minussubspace of $(Y,\mathfrak{S})$.

Furthermore, if $(X,\mathfrak{G})$ is an antisubspace of $(Y,\mathfrak{S})$, then $A \subset Y$ is $\mathfrak{S}$-compact implies that $A \cap X = A \setminus (Y \setminus X)$ is $\mathfrak{G}$-compact, since every centered subsystem of $\mathfrak{G}$ is a centered subsystem of $\mathfrak{S}$.

The following theorem corresponds to 1.8.

3.2. Theorem. Every C^*-space can be anti-embedded in a maximal compact space by the adjunction of one single point.

Proof. Let $(X,\mathfrak{G})$ be an arbitrary C^*-space and let p be a point which is not an element of X. We define $Y = X \cup \{p\}$ and

$$\mathfrak{S} = \mathfrak{G} \cup \{C \cup \{p\} \mid C \in \rho_X\mathfrak{G}\}.$$

It is easy to see that $(X,\mathfrak{G})$ is an antisubspace of the minusspace $(Y,\mathfrak{S})$.

In order to prove that $(Y,\mathfrak{S})$ is a compact space, we assume that $\mathfrak{S}'$ is a centered subsystem of $\mathfrak{S}$. If $\mathfrak{S}'$ does not contain a member of $\mathfrak{G}$, then $\bigcap \mathfrak{S}'$ contains p and thus the intersection of $\mathfrak{S}'$ is not empty. If $\mathfrak{S}'$ contains a member G_0 of $\mathfrak{G}$, then the system

$$\mathfrak{S}'' = \{S \cap G_0 | S \in \mathfrak{S}'\}$$

is centered and has the same intersection as the system $\mathfrak{S}'$. $\mathfrak{S}''$ is a subsystem of $\mathfrak{G}$. (For, if $A \in \mathfrak{G} = \rho_X^2\mathfrak{G}$ and $B \in \rho_X\mathfrak{G}$, then according to lemma I.2.4 we have both $A \cap B \in \rho\mathfrak{G}$ and $A \cap B \in \rho^2\mathfrak{G} = \mathfrak{G}$.) $(X,\mathfrak{G})$ is a C^*-space and hence a compact space. It follows that

$$\emptyset \neq \bigcap \mathfrak{S}'' = \bigcap \mathfrak{S}'.$$

We conclude that $(Y,\mathfrak{S})$ is compact.

In order to prove that $(Y,\mathfrak{S})$ is a CC-space, we assume that A is a compact subset of $(Y,\mathfrak{S})$. If A contains p, then $(A \setminus \{p\})$ must be compact relative to $\mathfrak{G}$ (cf. remark 3.1) and hence A is a member of $\mathfrak{S}$. If A does not contain p, then A is a subset of X which is compact relative to $\rho\mathfrak{G}$. Therefore $A \in \rho^2\mathfrak{G}$, i.e., $A \in \mathfrak{G}$. Consequently in both cases $A \in \mathfrak{S}$, and we conclude that $(Y,\mathfrak{S})$ is a compact CC-space (hence a topological space) and so by 1.7 is a maximal compact space.

<u>3.3. Lemma</u>. A minusspace $(X,\mathfrak{G})$ is an antispace if and only if the following two conditions are satisfied:

(i) There exists a minusspace $(X,\mathfrak{S})$ such that $\mathfrak{G} = \rho\mathfrak{S}$.

(ii) $\mathfrak{G}$ contains every subset of X which has a $\mathfrak{G}$-closed intersection with every $\mathfrak{G}$-compact subset of $(X,\mathfrak{G})$.

Proof. Suppose that $(X,\mathfrak{G})$ is an antispace. Then $\mathfrak{G} = \rho^2\mathfrak{G}$ and $\mathfrak{G}$ is the collection of compact subsets in $(X,\rho\mathfrak{G})$. If a set A has a $\mathfrak{G}$-closed intersection with every $\mathfrak{G}$-compact subset of X, then it is easily verified that A is $\rho\mathfrak{G}$-compact, i.e., $A \in \rho(\rho\mathfrak{G}) = \mathfrak{G}$.

Conversely, suppose that $(X,\mathfrak{G})$ is a minusspace which satisfies both conditions. Then $\mathfrak{G} = \rho\mathfrak{S}$ for some collection $\mathfrak{S}$ of subsets of X.

Hence

$$\rho^2\mathfrak{G} = \rho^3\mathfrak{S} \supset \rho\mathfrak{S} = \mathfrak{G} \text{ (cf. I.2.6)}$$

and therefore $\mathfrak{G} \subset \rho^2\mathfrak{G}$.

In order to prove that $\rho^2\mathfrak{G} \subset \mathfrak{G}$ we suppose that $A \in \rho^2\mathfrak{G}$. Then $A \in \rho^3\mathfrak{S}$ and $A \cap C$ is a member of $\rho\mathfrak{S} = \mathfrak{G}$ for every set $C \in \rho^2\mathfrak{S}$ (cf. I.2.10). Therefore A has an intersection belonging to $\mathfrak{G}$ with every member of $\rho\mathfrak{G}$ and this implies that A is closed. Hence $\rho^2\mathfrak{G} \subset \mathfrak{G}$ and we conclude that $(X,\mathfrak{G})$ is an antispace.

3.4. Theorem. An antisubspace of an antispace is an antispace and an antisubspace of a C^*-space is a C^*-space.

Proof. The proof of this theorem will be carried out by showing that properties (i) and (ii) of 3.3 and the property of compactness for minusspaces are inherited by antisubspaces.

Let $(X,\mathfrak{G})$ be a minusspace and let $(Y,\mathfrak{J})$ be an antisubspace of $(X,\mathfrak{G})$.

(i) Suppose that $\mathfrak{G} = \rho\mathfrak{S}$ for some collection $\mathfrak{S}$ of subsets of X. Then $\mathfrak{S}$ generates a minusspace $(X,\gamma\mathfrak{S})$. The minussubspace $(Y,\mathfrak{S}')$ of $(X,\gamma\mathfrak{S})$ with the relative minustopology has the family

$$\rho\mathfrak{S}' = \{C \mid C \subset Y \;\&\; C \in \rho\mathfrak{S}\}$$

as its collection of compact subsets, but this collection is equal to $\mathfrak{J}$ by definition. We conclude that if $\mathfrak{G}$ is the collection of compact subsets in some minusspace on X, then $\mathfrak{J}$ is the collection of compact subsets in some minusspace on Y.

(ii) Suppose that $\mathfrak{G}$ contains every subset of X which has a $\mathfrak{G}$-closed intersection with every member of $\rho_X\mathfrak{G}$. If C_0 is a subset of X which belongs to $\rho_X\mathfrak{G}$, then every subsystem of members of $\mathfrak{G}$ which is centered in C_0 has a non-void intersection with C_0. Therefore every subsystem of members of $\mathfrak{J}$ which is centered in C_0 has a non-empty intersection with C_0, and we conclude that C_0 is compact relative to $\mathfrak{J}$. Since every member of $\mathfrak{J}$ is contained in Y it follows that

$$C_0 \cap Y \in \rho_Y\mathfrak{J}.$$

Now let B be a subset of Y such that B has an intersection belonging to $\mathfrak{J}$ with every member of $\rho_Y\mathfrak{J}$. Then also

$$B \cap A \in \mathfrak{G} \text{ for all } A \in \rho_Y\mathfrak{J}.$$

Moreover, according to the preceding observation,

$$C \cap Y \in \rho_Y\mathfrak{J} \text{ for all } C \in \rho_X\mathfrak{G}.$$

Consequently,

$$B \cap C = (B \cap Y) \cap C = B \cap (Y \cap C) \in \mathfrak{G}$$

for all $C \in \rho_X\mathfrak{G}$.
Therefore $B \in \mathfrak{G}$. Since $B \subset Y$ this implies $B \in \mathfrak{J}$.

From (i), (ii) and lemma 3.3 we conclude that $(Y,\mathfrak{J})$ is an antispace whenever $(X,\mathfrak{G})$ is an antispace.

(iii) Now suppose that X is compact relative to $\mathfrak{G}$. Then every centered subsystem of $\mathfrak{G}$ has a non-empty intersection with X and hence every centered subsystem of $\mathfrak{J}$ has a non-empty intersection with Y. Thus Y is compact relative to $\mathfrak{J}$.

This means that $(Y,\mathfrak{J})$ is a compact antispace, i.e., a C^*-space whenever $(X,\mathfrak{G})$ is a C^*-space.

<u>3.5. Corollary</u>. If $(X,\mathfrak{G})$ is a C-space and $(Y,\mathfrak{S})$ is a subspace of $(X,\mathfrak{G})$, then $(Y,\rho\mathfrak{S})$ is both a C^*-space and an antisubspace of $(X,\rho\mathfrak{G})$ [although $(Y,\mathfrak{S})$ does not need to be a C-space].

<u>3.6. Proposition</u>. If $(X,\mathfrak{G})$ is a minusspace and $(Y,\mathfrak{S})$ is an antisubspace of $(X,\mathfrak{G})$ with the property that $X \setminus Y$ is compact relative to $\mathfrak{G}$, then

$$\rho_Y\mathfrak{S} = \{C \cap Y \mid C \in \rho_X\mathfrak{G}\}$$

and $(Y,\gamma\rho\mathfrak{S})$ is a minussubspace of $(X,\gamma\rho\mathfrak{G})$.

Proof. The collection $\mathfrak{S}$ is contained in $\mathfrak{G}$. Therefore, if C is compact relative to $\mathfrak{G}$, then every non-empty subsystem of $\mathfrak{S}$ which is centered in C has a non-empty intersection with C. This intersection is contained in Y and hence $C \cap Y$ is compact relative to $\mathfrak{S}$. Therefore

$$\{C \cap Y | C \in \rho_X \mathfrak{G}\} \subset \rho_Y \mathfrak{S}.$$

Next we suppose that K is a member of $\rho_Y \mathfrak{S}$, but $K \cup (X \setminus Y)$ is not a member of $\rho_X \mathfrak{G}$. Then there exists a subsystem $\mathfrak{G}'$ of $\mathfrak{G}$ which is centered in $K \cup (X \setminus Y)$ with the property that

$$(\cap \mathfrak{G}') \cap (K \cup (X \setminus Y)) = \emptyset.$$

In particular

$$(\cap \mathfrak{G}') \cap (X \setminus Y) = \emptyset,$$

and from the assumption that $X \setminus Y \in \rho_X \mathfrak{G}$, it follows that there exists a finite subfamily

$$\{G_i | i = 1, 2, \ldots, n\},$$

of $\mathfrak{G}'$ with the property that

$$(\bigcap_{i=1}^{n} G_i) \cap (X \setminus Y) = \emptyset.$$

If we let $G_0 = \bigcap_{i=1}^{n} G_i$, then $G_0 \subset Y$. Since $G_0 \in \mathfrak{G}$ this implies that $G_0 \in \mathfrak{S}$. The system

$$\mathfrak{G}'' = \{G \cap G_0 | G \in \mathfrak{G}'\}$$

is a subsystem of $\mathfrak{S}$ which is centered in K. From the assumption that K is $\mathfrak{S}$-compact it follows that

$$\emptyset \neq (\cap \mathfrak{G}'') \cap K = (\cap \mathfrak{G}') \cap (K \cup (X \setminus Y)).$$

This is a contradiction. Consequently, if $K \in \rho_Y \mathfrak{S}$, then $K \cup (X \setminus Y) \in \rho_X \mathfrak{G}$. We conclude that

$$\rho \mathfrak{S} \subset \{C \cap Y | C \in \rho_X \mathfrak{G}\}$$

and so

$$\rho_Y \mathfrak{S} = \{C \cap Y | C \in \rho_X \mathfrak{G}\}.$$

It now follows easily that $(Y,\gamma\rho_Y\mathfrak{S})$ is a subspace of $(X,\gamma\rho_X\mathfrak{G})$.

<u>3.7. Theorem</u>. Every antispace can be anti-embedded in a C-space by the adjunction of one single point. Moreover, every antispace can be embedded in a compact antispace by means of adjoining one point.

Proof. Let $(X,\mathfrak{G})$ be an antispace and suppose that p is a point which is not in X. Define $Z = X \cup \{p\}$. In order to find a minustopology $\mathfrak{S}$ on Z such that $(Z,\mathfrak{S})$ is a C-space which contains $(X,\mathfrak{G})$ as an antisubspace, we first define a minustopology $\tilde{\mathfrak{S}}$ on Z. Then we construct $\mathfrak{S}$ by means of $\tilde{\mathfrak{S}}$.

Define: $\tilde{\mathfrak{S}} = \gamma(\mathfrak{G} \cup \{C \cup \{p\} | C \in \rho_X\mathfrak{G}\}$.

First we observe that $(Z,\tilde{\mathfrak{S}})$ is a CC-space. For, if A is an $\tilde{\mathfrak{S}}$-compact subset of Z, then A is also $\mathfrak{G}$-compact and hence $A \cup \{p\} \in \tilde{\mathfrak{S}}$. If $p \in A$ this means that $A \in \tilde{\mathfrak{S}}$. If $p \notin A$ then it follows easily from the definition of $\tilde{\mathfrak{S}}$ that A is also $\rho_X\mathfrak{G}$-compact, i.e., $A \in \rho_X^2\mathfrak{G} = \mathfrak{G}$. In both cases $A \in \tilde{\mathfrak{S}}$, and we conclude that $\rho_Z\tilde{\mathfrak{S}} \subset \tilde{\mathfrak{S}}$, i.e., $(Z,\tilde{\mathfrak{S}})$ is a CC-space.

From 2.13 it follows that $(Z,\rho^2\tilde{\mathfrak{S}})$ is a C-space. If we consider X as a subset in the minusspace $(Z,\tilde{\mathfrak{S}})$, then the induced anti-relative topology in X equals $\mathfrak{G}$; if we consider X as a subset in the minusspace $(Z,\rho^2\tilde{\mathfrak{S}})$, then we denote by $\mathfrak{J}$ the induced anti-relative topology on X. Furthermore, $Z \setminus X = \{p\}$ is compact, both in $(Z,\tilde{\mathfrak{S}})$ and in $(Z,\rho^2\tilde{\mathfrak{S}})$. From proposition 3.6 it follows that

$$\rho\mathfrak{G} = \{C \cap X | C \in \rho\tilde{\mathfrak{S}}\}$$

and

$$\rho\mathfrak{J} = \{C \cap X | C \in \rho^3\tilde{\mathfrak{S}}\}.$$

Since $(Z,\tilde{\mathfrak{S}})$ is a CC-space, the proof of 2.11 implies that $\rho\tilde{\mathfrak{S}} = \rho^3\tilde{\mathfrak{S}}$ and hence we conclude that $\rho\mathfrak{G} = \rho\mathfrak{J}$ and so $\rho^2\mathfrak{G} = \rho^2\mathfrak{J}$. The space $(X,\mathfrak{J})$ is an antisubspace of the antispace $(Z,\rho^2\tilde{\mathfrak{S}})$ and thus theorem 3.4 implies that $(X,\mathfrak{J})$ is an antispace. Therefore we have

$$\mathfrak{G} = \rho^2\mathfrak{G} = \rho^2\mathfrak{J} = \mathfrak{J}$$

and $(X,\mathfrak{G})$ is an antisubspace of the C-space $(X,\rho^2\tilde{\mathfrak{S}})$.

We have proved now that every antispace can be anti-embedded in a C-space. Since $(X,\mathfrak{G})$ is an antispace, the space $(X,\gamma\rho\mathfrak{G}) = (X,\rho\mathfrak{G})$ is its anti-image. Moreover, since $\gamma\rho^2 = \rho^2$, we have $(Z,\gamma\rho^3\tilde{\mathfrak{S}}) = (Z,\rho^3\tilde{\mathfrak{S}}) = (Z,\gamma\rho\tilde{\mathfrak{S}}) = (Z,\rho\tilde{\mathfrak{S}})$. Consequently 3.6 implies that $(X,\rho\mathfrak{G})$ is a subspace of $(Z,\rho\tilde{\mathfrak{S}})$, while $(Z,\rho\tilde{\mathfrak{S}})$ is the anti-image of a C-space and hence a C^*-space.

The constructed compact antispace can be called the one point compactification of the antispace $(X,\rho\mathfrak{G})$. Observe that the collection of all complements of members of $\rho\mathfrak{G} \cap \mathfrak{G}$ is precisely the collection of all open sets of $(Z,\rho\tilde{\mathfrak{S}})$ which contain p.

<u>3.8. Corollary</u>. (i). The class of all antispaces is precisely the class of all antisubspaces of C-spaces and is precisely the class of all open subspaces of C^*-spaces.

(ii). The anti-image of an antisubspace of a C^*-space is equal to the C-expansion of the corresponding subspace of the corresponding C-space.

(iii). Let $(Y,\mathfrak{S})$ be a subspace of a C-space $(X,\mathfrak{G})$. Then both $(Y,\rho\mathfrak{S})$ and $(Y,\rho^2\mathfrak{S})$ are antispaces and $\mathfrak{S} \subset \rho^2\mathfrak{S}$.

Proof. Assertion (i) follows immediately from 3.4 and 3.7, (ii) follows from 3.5. Assertion (iii) is an easy consequence from (ii) and 2.10. It indicates another definition of a subspace of a C-space, namely, $(Y,\rho^2\mathfrak{S})$ can be considered as a <u>C-subspace</u> of $(X,\mathfrak{G})$ (compare with [10]). We will not investigate this notion any further in this treatise.

<u>3.9. Definition</u>. Let $\{(X_\alpha,\mathfrak{G}_\alpha)\}_{\alpha\in A}$ be a collection of minusspaces such that $X_\alpha \cap X_\beta = \emptyset$ if $\alpha \neq \beta$. Let $X = \bigcup_{\alpha\in A} X_\alpha$.

1) If $\mathfrak{G} = \{G \mid G \subset X \ \& \ (\forall\alpha \in A)(G \cap X_\alpha \in \mathfrak{G}_\alpha)\}$, then $(X,\mathfrak{G})$ is a minusspace. It is called the <u>minussum</u> of the collection $\{(X_\alpha,\mathfrak{G}_\alpha)\}_{\alpha\in A}$.

2) If $\mathfrak{S} = \gamma(\bigcup_{\alpha\in A} \mathfrak{G}_\alpha)$, then also $(X,\mathfrak{S})$ is a minusspace. It is called the <u>antisum</u> of the collection $\{(X_\alpha,\mathfrak{G}_\alpha)\}_{\alpha\in A}$.

Remark. If the collection A is finite, and if $\emptyset \in \mathfrak{G}_\alpha$ for all α, then the minussum coïncides with the antisum, but if A is infinite and if $\emptyset \in \mathfrak{G}_\alpha$ for all α, then the minustopology defined by the minussum is strictly finer than the minustopology induced by the antisum. If $\mathfrak{G}$ is an arbitrary closed set in the antisum, then $G \cap X_\alpha = \emptyset$ for all but a finite number of α's. Observe that if $\{(X_\alpha,\mathfrak{G}_\alpha)\}$ are antispaces, then $\emptyset \in \mathfrak{G}_\alpha$ for all α, since $\emptyset$ is always squarecompact. If $\{(X_\alpha,\mathfrak{G}_\alpha)\}$ are topological spaces, then the minussum coincides with the usual topological sum.

3.10. Theorem. The minussum and the antisum of a disjoint collection of antispaces are both antispaces. The anti-image of the minussum of a collection of antispaces equals the antisum of the anti-images of that collection of antispaces.

Proof. Let $\{(X_\alpha,\mathfrak{G}_\alpha) \mid \alpha \in A\}$ be an arbitrary collection of disjoint antispaces which is indexed by the set A. Let $(X,\mathfrak{G})$ be their minussum, and assume that $(X,\mathfrak{S})$ is the antisum of the collection of their anti-images:

$$\{(X_\alpha,\rho_{X_\alpha}\mathfrak{G}_\alpha) \mid \alpha \in A\}.$$

For convenience in the remainder of the proof, we use ρ_α to denote ρ_{X_α} and ρ_α^2 to denote $\rho_{X_\alpha}^2$.

In order to prove that $\mathfrak{S} = \rho_X\mathfrak{G}$ and $\mathfrak{G} = \rho_X\mathfrak{S}$ we prove in succession

(i) $\mathfrak{S} \subset \rho_X\mathfrak{G}$;

(ii) $\rho_X\mathfrak{G} \subset \mathfrak{S}$;

(iii) $\mathfrak{G} \subset \rho_X\mathfrak{S}$;

(iv) $\rho_X\mathfrak{S} \subset \mathfrak{G}$.

(i) Let $S \in \mathfrak{S}$ and let $\mathfrak{G}'$ be a subsystem of $\mathfrak{G}$ which is centered in S. Clearly S may be written in the form

$$S = C_{\alpha_0} \cup C_{\alpha_1} \cup \ldots \cup C_{\alpha_n},$$

where $C_{\alpha_i} \in \rho_{\alpha_i} \mathfrak{G}_{\alpha_i}$. Consequently $\mathfrak{G}'$ must be centered in at least one of the sets C_{α_i}. We may assume it is C_{α_0}. Now let

$$\mathfrak{G}'' = \{G \cap X_{\alpha_0} \mid G \in \mathfrak{G}'\}.$$

Then $\mathfrak{G}''$ is a subcollection of $\mathfrak{G}_{\alpha_0}$ and since $C_{\alpha_0} \in \rho_{\alpha_0} \mathfrak{G}_{\alpha_0}$ it follows that

$$(\cap \mathfrak{G}'') \cap C_{\alpha_0} \neq \emptyset.$$

Consequently,

$$\emptyset \neq (\cap \mathfrak{G}') \cap C_{\alpha_0} \subset (\cap \mathfrak{G}') \cap S$$

and hence $S \in \rho_X \mathfrak{G}$. We conclude that $\mathfrak{S} \subset \rho_X \mathfrak{G}$.

(ii) We first observe that $\emptyset \in \mathfrak{G}_\alpha$ for every α, since $(X_\alpha, \mathfrak{G}_\alpha)$ is an antispace. Consequently $\mathfrak{G}_\alpha \subset \mathfrak{G}$ for every α. Now, let T be a subset of X which is not a member of $\mathfrak{S}$. Then either there exists an index β such that $T \cap X_\beta \notin \rho_\beta \mathfrak{G}_\beta$, or we can define an infinite subset A_0 of A such that $T \cap X_\alpha \neq \emptyset$ if $\alpha \in A_0$. In the first case it follows from $\mathfrak{G}_\beta \subset \mathfrak{G}$, that there exists a subsystem $\mathfrak{G}'_\beta$ of $\mathfrak{G}_\beta$ which is centered in $T \cap X_\beta$, whereas

$$(\cap \mathfrak{G}'_\beta) \cap (T \cap X_\beta) = \emptyset.$$

Since every member of $\mathfrak{G}'_\beta$ is contained in X_β we have

$$(\cap \mathfrak{G}'_\beta) \cap T = \emptyset$$

and we conclude that $T \notin \rho_X \mathfrak{G}$.
In the second case we choose a point $p_\alpha \in X_\alpha \cap T$ for every $\alpha \in A_0$. For every $\alpha \in A_0$, let

$$P_\alpha = \{p_\beta \mid \beta \in A_0 \ \& \ \beta \neq \alpha\}.$$

Since $(X_\beta, \mathfrak{G}_\beta)$ is an antispace, p_β is squarecompact and hence closed in $(X_\beta, \mathfrak{G}_\beta)$ for every $\beta \in A_0$. Therefore P_α is a closed subset of $(X, \mathfrak{G})$. From the assumption that A_0 is infinite it follows that the collection

$\{P_\alpha | \alpha \in A_0\}$ is centered in T. However

$$(\cap \{P_\alpha | \alpha \in A_0\}) \cap T = \emptyset.$$

Consequently $T \notin \rho_X \mathfrak{G}$ in both cases and hence $\rho_X \mathfrak{G} \subset \mathfrak{S}$.

(iii) Let $G \in \mathfrak{G}$ and suppose that $\mathfrak{C}'$ is a subsystem of $\bigcup_{\alpha \in A} \rho_\alpha \mathfrak{G}_\alpha$ which is centered in G. Then $\mathfrak{C}'$ is centered and it follows that there exists an α_0, such that $\mathfrak{C}' \subset \rho_{\alpha_0} \mathfrak{G}_{\alpha_0}$, and

$$G \cap X_{\alpha_0} \in \mathfrak{G}_{\alpha_0} = \rho^2_{\alpha_0} \mathfrak{G}_{\alpha_0}.$$

Therefore $(\cap \mathfrak{C}') \cap G \neq \emptyset$, and hence

$$G \in \rho_X(\bigcup_{\alpha \in A} \rho_\alpha \mathfrak{G}_\alpha) = \rho_X \gamma(\bigcup_{\alpha \in A} \rho_\alpha \mathfrak{G}_\alpha) = \rho_X \mathfrak{S}.$$

We conclude that $\mathfrak{G} \subset \rho_X \mathfrak{S}$.

(iv) Suppose that $G \notin \mathfrak{G}$. Then there exists an index β such that $(G \cap X_\beta) \notin \mathfrak{G}_\beta$. Since $(X_\beta, \mathfrak{G}_\beta)$ is an antispace, this means exactly $(G \cap X_\beta) \notin \rho^2_\beta \mathfrak{G}_\beta$, and thus $G \cap X_\beta$ is not compact relative to $\rho_\beta \mathfrak{G}_\beta$. From $\rho_\beta \mathfrak{G}_\beta \subset \mathfrak{S}$ it now follows that $G \notin \rho_X \mathfrak{S}$ and so $\rho_X \mathfrak{S} \subset \mathfrak{G}$.

3.11. Remark. It is easy to see that the minussum of a collection of C-spaces is a C-space. In this case the minussum is equal to the topological sum of these spaces. Therefore the antisum of a collection of C^*-spaces is a C^*-space. However a minussum of an infinite collection of C^*-spaces is never a C^*-space. This yields another method to construct antispaces, e.g.; a minusspace with cofinite topology can be considered as the antisum of a collection of one point spaces, and hence it is a C^*-space. Its anti-image is the discrete space with the same cardinality. Furthermore, if $\{(X_\alpha, \mathfrak{G}_\alpha)\}_\alpha$ is an arbitrary collection of T_1 minusspaces, then the collection of compact subsets of their minussum induces the same minustopology as the antisum of the family of spaces $\{(X_\alpha, \gamma\rho_\alpha \mathfrak{G}_\alpha)\}_\alpha$, and also the collection of compact subsets of their antisum induces the same topology as the minussum of the family of spaces $\{(X_\alpha, \gamma\rho_\alpha \mathfrak{G}_\alpha)\}$. These statements can be proved similar to the proof of 3.10.

We will conclude this chapter with some propositions and remarks on continuous functions, quotient spaces and productspaces.

3.12. Definition. If X and Y are two minusspaces, then a function $f: X \to Y$ is called a k-mapping provided that the inverse image under f of a compact subset in Y is a compact subset of X.

3.13. Proposition. If $(X,\mathfrak{G})$ and $(Y,\mathfrak{S})$ are antispaces, then a function f from $(X,\mathfrak{G})$ to $(Y,\mathfrak{S})$ is continuous, if and only if f is a k-mapping from $(X,\rho\mathfrak{G})$ to $(Y,\rho\mathfrak{S})$.

Proof. Assume that f is a continuous function from $(X,\mathfrak{G})$ to $(Y,\mathfrak{S})$. Then the inverse image of a member of $\mathfrak{S}$ is a member of $\mathfrak{G}$. Since $\rho_Y^2\mathfrak{S} = \mathfrak{S}$ and $\rho_X^2\mathfrak{G} = \mathfrak{G}$ this means that the inverse image of a member of $\rho^2_Y\mathfrak{S} = \rho(\rho\mathfrak{S})$ is a member of $\rho(\rho\mathfrak{G})$ which implies that f is a k-mapping from $(X,\rho\mathfrak{G})$ to $(Y,\rho\mathfrak{S})$.

The converse is proved similarly.

3.14. Proposition. If the CC-space $(Y,\mathfrak{S})$ is a quotientspace of a C-space $(X,\mathfrak{G})$, then $(Y,\mathfrak{S})$ is a C-space.(This is a corollary of [7] p.240.)

Proof. Let f be a quotient mapping from $(X,\mathfrak{G})$ onto $(Y,\mathfrak{S})$ and suppose that S is a subset of Y which has a compact intersection with every closed compact subset of $(Y,\mathfrak{S})$. If we assume that S is not closed, then $f^{-1}[S]$ is not closed either and hence there exists a compact subset C of $(X,\mathfrak{G})$ such that $C \cap f^{-1}[S]$ is not compact in $(X,\mathfrak{G})$. The set $C \cap f^{-1}[S]$ is a non-compact subset of C. C is compact and hence closed. Consequently, $C \cap f^{-1}[S]$ is not closed. Therefore there exists a point p in the closure of $C \cap f^{-1}[S]$ which does not belong to $C \cap f^{-1}[S]$. It follows that $p \in C$ and hence $p \notin f^{-1}[S]$. This implies that

$$p \notin f^{-1}[S] \cap f^{-1}[f[C]] = f^{-1}[S \cap f[C]].$$

The set $f[C]$ is compact in $(Y,\mathfrak{S})$ and hence $f[C] \cap S$ is compact and closed in $(Y,\mathfrak{S})$ and therefore

$$f^{-1}[S \cap f[C]]$$

is closed in $(X,\mathfrak{G})$. Furthermore $C \subset f^{-1}[f[C]]$ and hence p is in the closure of $f^{-1}[S \cap f[C]]$. This is a contradiction. We conclude that

ERRATUM.

II. 3.15

Since the quotient mapping mentioned in example II. 3.15 is not closed, the question whether or not all closed continuous images of C-spaces are C-spaces is still open.

A quotient space of a C-space is a C-space iff every inverse image of a compact set is closed. (cf. II. 1.2 and II. 3.14.)

S is closed if and only if S has a compact intersection with every closed compact subset of $(Y,\mathfrak{S})$ and hence $(Y,\mathfrak{S})$ is a C-space.

3.15. Remark. This proposition can be seen as a corollary of the well known result that the quotient spaces of a k-space are k-spaces (cf. [7]). It is natural to ask if every quotient space of a C-space is a C-space or, in particular, if a closed continuous image of a C-space is a C-space. By means of the following counterexample we will show that this is not the case.

Example. Consider the space consisting of two convergent sequences $\{p_i | i \in N\}$ and $\{q_i | i \in N\}$ with limit points p_0 and q_0 respectively.It is easy to see that this space is a C-space.

Let $\{r_i | i \in N\}$ be a sequence converging to two points r_0 and r_∞. Now we can define a mapping f which maps both p_i and q_i onto r_i for every $i \neq 0$ and which maps p_0 onto r_0 and q_0 onto r_∞. It is easy to see that f is a closed continuous mapping, but the quotient space is not a C-space.

Until now we have not mentioned product spaces of C-spaces. We can investigate a notion of C-product by defining the C-product of a collection of C-spaces as the C-expansion of the usual topological product of those spaces. This is actually carried out by N.E. Steenrod [10] forthe case of Hausdorff C-spaces. We shall not carry this investigations any further in this treatise.

Chapter III

Characterization of the notion of compactness

In this chapter we investigate three problems concerning the notion of compactness in the class of Tychonoff spaces, in the class of C-spaces and in the class of all minusspaces. In the first section a characterization of the class of all compact Hausdorff spaces is given. The characterization is in terms of heredity for certain topological operations.

The second problem concerns the characterization of the compactness operator. We will give conditions for an arbitrary operator defined on the collection of closed subsets of a Tychonoff space, resp., a C-space to be the compactness operator.

In the second section of this chapter we investigate the third problem which can be formulated as follows: Let X be a set and let $\mathfrak{C}$ be a collection of subsets of X. Find necessary and sufficient conditions for $\mathfrak{C}$ which guarantee that $\mathfrak{C}$ is the collection of all compact subsets relative to a suitably chosen system $\mathfrak{S}$ of subsets of X. Observe that, without loss of generality, $\mathfrak{S}$ may be a minustopology or a topology on X.

We conclude this section with a set of unsolved problems.

1. Characterization of compact spaces and the compactness operator

1.1. Theorem (DE GROOT). Let Γ be a class of topological spaces which satisfies the following conditions:

(i) The topological product of any collection of members of Γ is a member of Γ. (Productively closed).

(ii) Every closed subspace of a member of Γ is a member of Γ. (Hereditarily closed).

(iii) If $X \in \Gamma$ and $Y \in \Gamma$ and if X is a subspace of Y, then X is a closed subspace of Y. (Absolutely closed).

(iv) Every closed continuous image of a member of Γ is a member of Γ.

(v) The class Γ contains a space consisting of more than one point.

Then Γ is precisely the class of all compact Hausdorff spaces.

Proof. First we prove that every member of the class is Hausdorff. Suppose that X is a member of Γ, then $X \times X$ is also a member of Γ (cf. condition (i)). The subspace of $X \times X$ consisting of all points $\{(x,x) \mid x \in X\}$ is homeomorphic with X itself and hence a member of Γ. Condition (iii) implies that this subspace is closed in $X \times X$ and so the space X is a Hausdorff space. We conclude that every member of Γ is a Hausdorff space.

Next we prove that the class of all compact Hausdorff spaces is a subclass of Γ. Let X be a member of Γ which consists of more than one point (cf. condition (v)). Since X is Hausdorff it contains a closed discrete subspace consisting of two points. From condition (ii) it follows that the discrete space consisting of two points is a member of Γ. The Cantor set is homeomorphic with the countable product of discrete two point spaces, and so according to (i) it is a member of Γ. The closed unit interval is a closed continuous image of the Cantor space and hence it is contained in Γ (cf. condition (iv)). Moreover, every product of closed unit intervals is contained in Γ (cf. condition (i)) and since every compact Hausdorff space is a closed subspace of a product of closed intervals, it follows that every compact Hausdorff space belongs to Γ.

Next we prove that every member of Γ is a compact Hausdorff space. We know already that every member is Hausdorff; we only have to prove that every member is compact. Suppose that $(Y,\mathfrak{T})$ is a member of Γ and suppose that G_1 and G_2 are two disjoint closed subsets of $(Y,\mathfrak{T})$. We define a mapping f from Y into the power set of Y in the following way:

(i) $f(p) = G_1$ iff $p \in G_1$,

(ii) $f(p) = G_2$ iff $p \in G_2$,

(iii) $f(p) = \{p\}$ iff $p \notin G_1 \cup G_2$.

Then the set $f[Y]$ can be supplied with the quotient topology $\mathfrak{T}'$ with respect to Y and f. It is then easy to see that the function f is a closed continuous mapping from $(Y,\mathfrak{T})$ onto its quotient space $(f[Y],\mathfrak{T}')$. We conclude that $(f[Y],\mathfrak{T}')$ is a member of Γ and hence a Hausdorff space. In particular there exist two disjoint neighbourhoods U and V of the points $f[G_1]$ and $f[G_2]$ in the topological space $(f[Y],\mathfrak{T}')$. It follows that $f^{-1}[U]$ and $f^{-1}[V]$ are disjoint neighbourhoods of the closed sets G_1 and G_2 in $(Y,\mathfrak{T})$. Hence we conclude that $(Y,\mathfrak{T})$ is normal. Therefore $(Y,\mathfrak{T})$ has a Čech-Stone compactification $(Z,\mathfrak{Z})$. Since $(Z,\mathfrak{Z})$ is a compact Hausdorff space it belongs to Γ. Then it follows from condition (iii) that $(Y,\mathfrak{T})$ is closed in $(Z,\mathfrak{Z})$. This means that $(Y,\mathfrak{T})$ coïncides with $(Z,\mathfrak{Z})$ and consequently is a compact Hausdorff space.

<u>1.2. Theorem</u>. If we have for every set X an operator σ_X from $\mathfrak{P}(\mathfrak{P}(X))$ into itself, then σ_X coincides with ρ_X for the collection of all closed subsets of all Tychonoff spaces if and only if σ meets the following requirements:

(i) : If $\mathfrak{G}$ is the collection of closed sets in a Tychonoff space $(X,\mathfrak{T})$ then $\sigma_X\mathfrak{G} \subset \mathfrak{G}$. (Closedness condition).

(ii) : If $(A,\mathfrak{T}_A)$ is a subspace of $(X,\mathfrak{T})$ and $\mathfrak{G}_A$ is the collection of closed subsets of $(A,\mathfrak{T}_A)$ then $\sigma_A\mathfrak{G}_A = \{C \mid C \subset A \ \&\ C \in \sigma_X\mathfrak{G}\}$. (Subspace condition).

(iii): For every operator λ which assigns to the collection of closed subsets of every Tychonoff space another collection of subsets of the same space and which satisfies (i) and (ii) (with σ replaced by λ) then $\sigma_X\mathfrak{G} \supset \lambda_X\mathfrak{G}$ for the collection $\mathfrak{G}$ of closed sets in every Tychonoff space $(X,\mathfrak{T})$. (Maximality condition).

Proof. Let σ be an operator satisfying (i), (ii) and (iii). We prove that $\sigma_X\mathfrak{G} = \rho_X\mathfrak{G}$ for the collection $\mathfrak{G}$ of closed subsets of every Tychonoff space $(X,\mathfrak{T})$. We observe that every compact subset of a Tychonoff space is closed and hence $\rho_X(\mathfrak{G}) \subset \mathfrak{G}$. This means, that ρ satisfies condition (i). It is also well known that a subset of a topological space is compact if and only if it is compact in its relative topology. This implies that ρ satisfies condition (ii). We now apply (iii) to ρ and σ and obtain

$$\rho_X\mathfrak{G} \subset \sigma_X\mathfrak{G}$$

for the collection $\mathfrak{G}$ of closed subsets of every Tychonoff space.

On the other hand, we know that for every compact Hausdorff space $\rho\mathfrak{G} = \mathfrak{G}$ and therefore condition (i) implies that for compact Hausdorff spaces $\rho\mathfrak{G} \supset \sigma\mathfrak{G}$. From the fact that every Tychonoff space can be embedded in a compact Hausdorff space and from condition (ii) it follows that $\rho_A\mathfrak{G}_A \supset \sigma_A\mathfrak{G}_A$ for every subspace $(A,\mathfrak{T}_A)$ of a compact Hausdorff space $(X,\mathfrak{T})$.

We conclude that $\rho\mathfrak{G} \supset \sigma\mathfrak{G}$ for every Tychonoff space and hence $\rho = \sigma$ on this class.

<u>1.3. Remark</u>. The preceding theorem remains true if we replace the class of Tychonoff spaces by separable metric spaces. This follows easily from the fact, that every separable metric space can be embedded in the Hilbert cube - which is a compact metric space.

It is not known if the theorem is true for CC-spaces since it is still an open question whether or not every CC-space can be embedded in a maximal compact space.

1.4. Theorem. If we have for every set X an operator σ_X from $\mathfrak{P}(\mathfrak{P}(X))$ into itself, then σ_X coincides with ρ_X for the collections of all closed subsets of all C-spaces iff σ meets the following requirements:

(i) If $\mathfrak{G}$ is the collection of closed sets in any C-space $(X,\mathfrak{G})$, then $\sigma_X\mathfrak{G} \subset \mathfrak{G}$. (Closedness condition).

(ii) If $(A,\mathfrak{G}_A)$ is an open subspace of $(X,\mathfrak{G})$, then $\sigma_A\mathfrak{G}_A =$ $= \{C \mid C \subset A \ \& \ C \in \sigma_X\mathfrak{G}\}$. (Open subspace condition).

(iii) For every operator λ which assigns to the collection of closed subsets in every C-space another collection of subsets of the same space and which satisfies (i) and (ii) (with σ replaced by λ), then $\lambda\mathfrak{G} \subset \sigma\mathfrak{G}$ for the collection $\mathfrak{G}$ of closed subsets of every C-space. (Maximality condition).

Proof. The proof of this theorem is similar to the proof of 1.2; we merely have to replace "compact Hausdorff" by "maximal compact" and "subspace" by "open subspace". Then the theorem follows from II.1.8 and II.1.10.

1.5. Remark. This theorem remains true if we replace the notion of "C-space" by the notion of "locally compact Hausdorff space". At this moment we do not know a method for characterizing the compactness operator in the class of all topological spaces.

2. Collections of compact subsets and problems

In this section we will make some remarks on the following problem: Given a set X, characterize all collections $\mathfrak{C}$ of subsets of X which are the collections of compact subsets relative to some other family of subsets of X. This problem seems to be difficult and remains unsolved in its generality. However, we start this section with some necessary conditions for the collections $\mathfrak{C}$. Furthermore a characterization of all collections $\mathfrak{C}$ which are the collections of compact subsets of antispaces is derived as a corollary of the previous chapter.

2.1. Proposition. Let X be a set and let $\mathfrak{C}$ be a collection of subsets of X such that $\mathfrak{C}$ is the collection of compact subsets in some topology on X. Then

(i) $\rho^2\mathfrak{C} \supset \mathfrak{C}$.

(ii) The intersection of a member of $\mathfrak{C}$ with a member of $\rho\mathfrak{C}$ is a member of $\mathfrak{C}$.

(iii) Every infinite member of $\mathfrak{C}$ contains an infinite proper subset which is also a member of $\mathfrak{C}$.

(iv) $\mathfrak{C}$ is closed under the taking of finite unions and every finite subset A of X is a member of $\mathfrak{C}$.

Proof. $\mathfrak{C} = \rho\mathfrak{G}$ for some collection $\mathfrak{G}$ of subsets of X. Without loss of generality we may assume that $\mathfrak{G}$ is the collection of closed subsets in some topology on X. Now the first assertion is precisely proposition I.2.6 and the second assertion is precisely lemma I.2.4. In order to prove (iii) we assume that A is an infinite member of $\mathfrak{C}$ which does not contain a proper infinite subset belonging to $\mathfrak{C}$. For every $G \in \mathfrak{G}$ we have that $G \cap A$ belongs to $\mathfrak{C}$, which implies that $G \cap A$ is finite or $G \cap A = A$. Now let B be an arbitrary proper subset of A. Then $G \cap B$ is finite or $G \cap B = B$ for every $G \in \mathfrak{G}$. This means that B is $\mathfrak{G}$-compact and hence a member of $\mathfrak{C}$. So from the assumption that no infinite subset of A belongs to $\rho\mathfrak{G} = \mathfrak{C}$, we have derived that every subset of A belongs to $\rho\mathfrak{G} = \mathfrak{C}$. This is a contradiction. Consequently for every

infinite set $A \in \mathfrak{C}$ there exists a proper subset of A which is infinite and which is a member of $\mathfrak{C}$.
The fourth assertion is well known.

<u>2.2. Remark</u>. It is easy to see that condition (i) of the preceding proposition follows from condition (ii). If we assume that $\gamma\mathfrak{C} = \mathfrak{C}$ then condition (ii) also implies condition (iii).

Furthermore we show by means of a counterexample that the conditions of 2.1 are not sufficient.

<u>Example</u>. Let X be an uncountable set and let $\mathfrak{C}$ be the collection of all countable subsets of X. Then $\rho\mathfrak{C}$ consists of all finite subsets of X and every subset of X is a member of $\rho^2\mathfrak{C}$. Hence conditions (i) and (ii) are fulfilled. It is easy to see that $\mathfrak{C}$ also satisfies conditions (iii) and (iv) of 2.1.

In order to prove that $\mathfrak{C}$ is not the collection of compact subsets relative to any family $\mathfrak{S}$, we assume that $\mathfrak{S}$ is a collection of subsets of X and that $\rho\mathfrak{S} = \mathfrak{C}$.
From Alexander's theorem it follows that we may assume without loss of generality that $\gamma\mathfrak{S} = \mathfrak{S}$. The set X itself is not compact and hence there exists a nest $\mathfrak{N} \subset \mathfrak{S}$ such that $\emptyset \notin \mathfrak{N}$ and $\bigcap \mathfrak{N} = \emptyset$. Now choose a point $p_1 \in X$ and a set $N_1 \in \mathfrak{N}$ such that $p_1 \notin N_1$. Then we choose a point $p_2 \in N_1$ and a set $N_2 \in \mathfrak{N}$ such that $p_2 \notin N_2$. We proceed by choosing $p_i \in N_{i-1}$ and $N_i \in \mathfrak{N}$ such that $p_i \notin N_i$. The set $\{p_i\}_{i=1}^{\infty}$ is a countable subset of X and the collection $\{N_i\}_{i=1}^{\infty}$ is centered in $\{p_i\}_{i=1}^{\infty}$, whereas

$$(\{p_i\}_{i=1}^{\infty}) \cap (\bigcap_{i=1}^{\infty} N_i) = \emptyset.$$

It follows that the set $\{p_i\}_{i=1}^{\infty}$ is countable but not $\mathfrak{S}$-compact. This is a contradiction. We conclude that there exist no collection of subsets $\mathfrak{S}$ of X such that $\rho\mathfrak{S} = \mathfrak{C}$.

<u>2.3. Proposition</u>. A collection $\mathfrak{C}$ of subsets of a set X is the collection of compact subsets of an antispace X if and only if $(X,\mathfrak{C})$ is an antispace. A collection of subsets $\mathfrak{C}$ of a set X is the collection

of compact sets of some CC-space on X if and only if $(X,\mathfrak{S})$ is a C^*-space.

Proof. Follows immediately from II.2.5 and II.2.10.

2.4. Problems.

(i) Is it possible to embed an arbitrary CC-space in a maximal compact space?

(ii) If X is a set and $\mathfrak{S}$ is a collection of subsets of X, does $\rho\mathfrak{S} = \gamma\rho\mathfrak{S}$ imply that $\rho\mathfrak{S} = \rho^3\mathfrak{S}$?

(iii) If X is a set and $\mathfrak{S}$ is a collection of subsets of X such that $\rho\mathfrak{S} = \gamma\rho\mathfrak{S}$ and $\rho^2\mathfrak{S} \subset \rho\mathfrak{S}$, does this imply that $X \in \rho\mathfrak{S}$?

(iv) Let X be a set, and $\mathfrak{S}$ a collection of subsets such that $\gamma\rho_X\mathfrak{S} = \rho_X\mathfrak{S}$. Let $A \in \rho_X^3\mathfrak{S}$. Is it true that under these conditions A is a member of $\rho_A^3\mathfrak{T}$, where $\mathfrak{T}$ is the collection of closed sets in the relative minustopology on A?

Remark. It is easy to see that (ii) is equivalent with (iii) & (iv).

(v) Let $(X,\mathfrak{T})$ and $(Y,\mathfrak{Y})$ be two C-spaces. Is it true that the intersection of two compact sets of their topological product is compact in the product topology?

REFERENCES

[1] A. ARHANGEL'SKII — Bicompact sets and the topology of spaces. Dokl. Akad. Nauk. SSSR. 150 (1963) p. 9-12. Soviet Mathematics 4 (1963) p. 561-564.

[2] A. ARHANGEL'SKII. — On embeddings of T_1 spaces in bicompact T_1 spaces of the same weight. Bull. Acad. Pol. des Sci. 14 (1966) p. 361-366.

[3] P. van EMDE BOAS et al. — De onderlinge afhankelijkheid van een aantal topologische axioma's die verband houden met het k-axioma. Mathematisch Centrum Amsterdam. Report WN 18 (1965).

[4] J. de GROOT. — An isomorphism principle in general topology. Bull. Am. Math. Soc. 73 (1967) p. 465-467.

[5] J. de GROOT, G.E. STRECKER, E. WATTEL. — The compactness operator in general topology. Proc. 2nd. Symposium on Topology Prague. (1967) p. 161-163.

[6] J. de GROOT, H. HERRLICH, G.E. STRECKER, E. WATTEL. — Compactness as an operator. Issued for publication.

[7] J.L. KELLEY. — General Topology. Van Nostrand 1955.

[8] N. SMYTHE, C.A. WILKINS. — Minimal Hausdorff and maximal compact spaces. Journ. Austr. Math. Soc. 3 (1963) p. 167-171.

[9] E.H. SPANIER. — Algebraic topology, Mac Graw-Hill (1966).

[10] N.E. STEENROD. A convenient category of topological spaces. Mich. Math. Journal 14-2 (1967) p. 133-152.

[11] G.E. STRECKER, E. WATTEL, H. HERRLICH, J. de GROOT. Strengthening Alexander's subbase theorem. To appear in Duke Math. Journal.

[12] E. WATTEL, G.E. STRECKER. On the compactness operator in general topology. Mathematisch Centrum Amsterdam. Report WN 22 (1966).

SUBJECT INDEX

Alexander's theorem 4
anti-embedding 38
anti-image 33
antipair 33
anti-relative minustopology 38
antispace 33
antisubspace 38
antisum 44
Bacon's lemma 20
CC-space 26
centered system 2
C-expansion 37
closed base 2
closed subbase 2
closed subset of a minusspace 32
closure 33
compact relative to 𝔖 3
compactly generated space 26
compact minusspace 34
compactness operator 6
C-space 26
C^*-space 34
C-subspace 44
k-expansion 36
Key lemma 3
k-mapping 48
k-space 26
maximal compact space 28
minusspace 32
minussubspace 38
minussum 44
minustopology 32
open subset of a minusspace 32
operator γ 6
operator ρ 6
relative minustopology 38
𝔖-compact 3
squarecompact relative to 𝔖 7
𝔖-squarecompact 7